The Mind Factor

Books by Jean Rosenbaum, M.D.

LOVE IN A DYING WORLD

ARISE SOLOMON

BECOMING YOURSELF

PRACTICAL PSYCHIATRY

IS YOUR VOLKSWAGEN A SEX SYMBOL?

THE PSYCHIATRIST'S COOKBOOK (WITH VERYL ROSENBAUM)

WHAT IS FEAR?

THE MIND FACTOR

How Your Emotions Affect Your Health

by
JEAN ROSENBAUM, M.D.

PRENTICE-HALL, INC.
Englewood Cliffs, New Jersey

The Mind Factor: How Your Emotions Affect Your Health by Jean Rosenbaum, M.D.

Prentice-Hall International, Inc., London
Prentice-Hall of Australia, Pty. Ltd., North Sydney
Prentice-Hall of Canada, Ltd., Toronto
Prentice-Hall of India Private Ltd., New Delhi
Prentice-Hall of Japan, Inc., Tokyo

Library of Congress Cataloging in Publication Data

Rosenbaum, Jean.
    The mind factor.

    1. Medicine, Psychosomatic. 2. Emotions.
I. Title. [DNLM: 1. Psychosomatic medicine—Popular
works. 2. Psychophysiologic disorders—Popular works.
WM 90 R81m   1972 (P)]
RC49.R67   616.08   72–8506
ISBN 0–13–583278–0

To Marcia Muth Miller,
for her tireless efforts

CONTENTS

Introduction

When the term *psychosomatic* became a popular household word some twenty years ago, it seemed like a very novel concept. For as medical specialization had become increasingly scientific in the early twentieth century and diseases of the physical body (the *soma*) more treatable, so had physicians increasingly separated the problems of the mind (the *psyche*) from medicine. It was as if the mind were not a part of the body but rather a near-magical function suspended somewhere off in space. And the practitioners of psychotherapy were often treated with as much disdain as were the patients.

Gradually, through the depth-psychology findings of psychoanalysis, these strange and seemingly senseless disorders of the mind became understandable and predictable. Within forty years, psychiatry caught up with the rest of medicine, and the natural outcome of such an equality of knowledge was that body and mind should come back together—as if they had not actually been joined all the time.

The human being was finally viewed as a physical and psychological entity. More important, it was at last understood that these two aspects of the whole person were interdependent, each causing major effects upon the other. The science of psychosomatics was born.

Psychosomatics created a lot of excitement in medical and psychiatric circles, for it clearly showed the distinctly emotional basis for a small number of difficult medical problems such as asthma. Whole new vistas were opened up. In addition to the basic discovery of psychoanalysis, psychosomatics promised to become one of the most significant findings in psychology in hundreds of years. And it has turned out that the value of psychosomatics was even then vastly underestimated. Literally thousands of scientific books and articles have been published in this field in the past quarter-century . . . and it has become a kind of specialty within psychiatry.

However, despite all the research and growth, there has been little written specifically for the lay public. Now that the field of psychosomatics has matured, it is time for a comprehensive work on the subject, one that the average person can grasp and be able to apply to himself and others. For the dynamics of a host of psychosomatic disorders have been well laid out, and many of these problems can be worked out by the sick individual without the help of a psychiatrist.

That, then, is the aim of this book: not only to define and explain psychosomatic problems, but to give definite and specific advice and guidelines for the alleviation of these often crippling disorders. This is a volume on practical everyday psychosomatics; it offers definitive programs for teaching the lay reader how his mind can help his body.

I

What Are Psychosomatic Symptoms?

Sorrow, Sickness, and a Troubled Mind

> *Let sorrow, sickness, and a troubled mind*
> *Be stranger to thee.*

This hope, voiced by Francis Quarles in the seventeenth century, has been a constant concern of doctors and others from ancient times to the present. Only within the last hundred years, however, has there been a concerted effort to treat ills that, though exhibited in the body, have their origins in the mind.

Psychosomatics is that branch of medical science which is concerned with illness in association with the state of mind.

Yes, sorrow, sickness, and a troubled mind do relate to one another. As you will see in these chapters, there may be a direct connection between your headache and your disappointment with your marriage partner. There may be a strong correlation between your heart-trouble symptoms and your fear of failure.

If your physical illness is psychosomatic in origin, discovering its cause can help you overcome the handicap which that illness imposes on your life.

Some Important Definitions

The following psychiatric definitions will help you get the most out of this book.

Psychosomatic—This word is actually two terms combined: *psyche,* the mind, and *soma,* the body. Thus, the word *psychosomatic* means mind and body considered as one, inseparable. It is a term of interrelationship.

Psychotherapy—The treatment of mental or emotional ills including psychosomatic illnesses.

Psychoanalysis—A system of psychotherapy developed by Sigmund Freud. It is the study and interpretation of mental states and drives.

Psychoanalyst—A doctor who is trained in psychoanalytic technique and uses it in psychotherapy.

Ego—A psychological division of the mind. It is the conscious part, of which you are most aware.

Ego Ideals System—Your goals, morals, and ethical values; part of your superego.

Id—A psychological division of the mind. Part of your unconscious, the id contains the instinctual and aggressive drives.

Superego—The third psychological division of the mind and part of the unconscious. It contains your *ego ideals and guilt systems.*

Preconscious—Refers to that area of the mind where repressed memories are just below the level of awareness but can be recalled into consciousness.

Conscious—A level of mental awareness. This awareness is about one's self and about the external world as well.

Unconscious—That part of the mind which contains primitive and repressed memories, as well as impulses. It is not on a level of awareness.

Conflict—A clash resulting from contradictory impulses or from differences between inner drives and the demands of the world in which one lives. Conflict often occurs between the ego and the id, or between the ego and the superego.

Emotional Response—A response by the individual which includes feelings, overt signs, and physiological changes.

Complex—Emotionally interrelated memories, desires, and feelings that acting together may dominate the personality.

Personality—The total sum of the characteristics of an individual.

Compulsion—An irresistible impulse to perform some physical act.

Hypochondriasis—A persistent and abnormal anxiety and concern about one's health. It is usually accompanied by imagined pains, illnesses, and body malfunctions.

Hysteria—An overt expression of an emotional conflict. It is a form of psychoneurosis.

Psychoneurosis or *Neurosis*—A mental disorder that comes from an unconscious effort to adjust by making some compromise to an existing conflict.

Syndrome—A set of symptoms relating to a disease or disorder.

Anxiety—A tense, emotional state characterized by fear and painful uncertainty.

Repression—An unconscious process by which ideas, desires, and memories that are considered to be too painful, unpleasant, or unacceptable are excluded from consciousness.

Trauma—A severe, often violent, emotional shock that results in damage to the personality.

How Emotional Conflicts Are Expressed in Physical Language

Your emotional conflicts need an outlet. That outlet can be in the form of psychosomatic illnesses.

Repression of a drive may result in a physical illness that is psychosomatic in origin. You may think you have been successful in deceiving yourself and others about your causes for conflict, but your body is telling you the truth.

Your emotional conflicts become physical symptoms through a unique and personal mental process. You actually select your particular illness or disease and then develop appropriate symptoms. This is an unconscious process on your part.

A trained analyst, however, can trace his way through the labyrinth of your mind to the source and cause of your psychosomatic illness.

Why Are Emotional Conflicts Expressed in Body Language?

Having a sickness has always been more socially acceptable than having a temper tantrum. In a success-oriented world, it is excusable to explain away failure on the grounds of physical disability.

Indirection is the root of psychosomatic illness. The patient does not say "I hate my father" or "I dislike my job," but he does say "I have these blinding headaches" or "I've developed this ulcer."

Children may have tantrums when they don't get their own way. Or to express their anxiety or their dissatisfaction, they may vomit, wet, or soil themselves. Anti-social or anti-adult acts may include breaking objects, screaming, and running away from people.

Adults are not permitted to behave in these ways. To express their emotional conflicts, they may develop an array of acceptable and believable physical symptoms.

"Body Chatter" and Why It Is Important to Know How to Decode It

You can listen to your "body-chatter" and learn some important and revealing things about yourself.

A patient who said "I don't understand why I have these frequent attacks of indigestion" was telling the truth. One reason he didn't understand was that he had never really stopped to listen to what his body was trying to tell him. When he did, he discovered for himself that his attacks of indigestion coincided with visits from an uncle whom he disliked because of an early childhood incident.

Decoding your body-chatter can save you days of misery, pain, and unhappiness.

Body chatter indicates that there is trouble. It may be expressing your hidden fears, tensions, anxieties, worries, and guilt feelings.

Don't be afraid to listen to body-chatter. Decoding it could change your life!

Ways in Which Your Body Talks to You

Perhaps it would be better to say "ways in which your body talks *back* to you."

Headache, dizziness, hives, allergies, breathing difficulties, blood-pressure fluctuations, chest pains, cramps, indigestion, diarrhea, constipation, frequent urination, and sudden loss of sexual function are only some of the possible psychosomatic symptoms.

They are counterfeit symptoms in the sense that they are imitating those caused by organic diseases. Yet they are real because they cause real pain and suffering.

You may have only one symptom or combination of symptoms.

How the Split Between Body and Mind Occurred in Medical History

Although some forms of psychological treatment have been used since man first became a thinking and ailing being, psychotherapy has become a science only in the last ninety years. Freud's discoveries gave this science the impetus to grow rapidly in importance and use.

Early Greek and Roman physicians recognized the close connection between mind and soul and body. But time and history marched on and the physical sciences and evolving technology began to claim the center of the stage. The new developments and advances in medicine were all related to improved techniques, advanced knowledge about the human body, and new drugs and vaccines.

Ridding the world of devastating plagues and diseases became the goal. Patients were treated for physical ills on a physical basis only.

Observant doctors, under the leadership of Freud and other pioneers in psychological studies, began to notice that in psychological studies, that some patients failed to get well even when all the proper means of treatment were used. Or if cured of one ailment, they promptly developed another.

Gradually it came to be realized that the *whole* man had to be treated. Today, the patient with severe headaches, stomach trouble, or any complaint of physical disability or discomfort has a better chance of regaining his total health because he is examined as a total person.

Freud himself did not claim to have discovered many new ideas, but he did originate invaluable concepts of understanding and treatment. In fact, he once said, "The poets and philosophers before me discovered the unconscious; what I discovered was the scientific method by which the unconscious can be studied."

Psychosomatics in the Pre-Psychiatric Era

In the pre-psychiatric era, psychosomatic illness was usually handled on a hit-and-miss basis. Patients who were cured were frequently cured by accident rather than design.

Actual mental disorders were considered to be cases of demoniacal possession. Treatment was often only a rite of exorcism. When psychosomatic illnesses were treated at all, it was most often by such methods as hypnotism, magic, and other forms of sorcery.

The average person who suffered from a psychosomatic illness could usually only pray and hope for relief. It was a rare individual who was perceptive enough to understand the relationship between his mind and his body, a relationship that is sometimes so subtle that it is difficult even for a trained observer to trace.

Were people never cured in those dark days? Undoubtedly some were, particularly if they had a strong enough faith in the means of cure, whether it was witchcraft, magic, religious miracles, or hypnotism. There were probably sufficient cures based on faith to keep the sufferer hopeful.

Witch Doctors and Their Magic

Witch doctors, medicine men, and a host of other non-scientific healers have always been available. Even today they are still present under various names. A troubled person would not today consult a witch doctor, but he might go to a medium or a faith healer. The principle, however, is still the same.

People suffering from psychosomatic illnesses are particularly inclined to seek help along unorthodox lines. They may have exhausted the limits and patience of medical doctors. They may have resisted attempts to cure them.

In ancient times and in primitive societies, only witch doctors or medicine men were available. These men, who were often the most learned in their tribe or community, had a rudimentary knowledge of basic psychological principles. Their claim to being able to drive out the evil spirits that were causing illness was one that could be substantiated by successful cases.

From our vantage-point in time and history, we can see that most of the illnesses that were cured must have been psychosomatic in origin. It is obvious that a "patient" who had severe chest pains of psychosomatic origin would recover if two conditions were present: He had to believe in the power of the witch doctor or medicine man, and the witch doctor had to perform some rites or give the patient something to eat, drink, wear, or do. These rites or instructions reinforced the patient's belief in the mysterious powers of the "doctor," and through strong enough belief psychosomatic illnesses were sometimes cured. On the other hand, a person who had severe chest pains because of an organic heart condition would not have been helped by any kind of magic ceremony.

Thus, medical missionaries have always been able to

help natives suffering from organic ills and diseases. They have conspicuously failed when faced with psychosomatic illnesses. The explanation is that their native patients simply did not have the same degree of faith and belief in them that they had in the tribal witch doctor.

Miracles and Faith

By and large, miracles are successful in proportion to the degree of faith the ill person has. Miracles are the result of willing belief.

Psychosomatic illnesses respond very well to suggestion of the possibility of a miracle. This faith and devotion to an ideal is responsible for the popularity and success of such places as Lourdes.

Miraculous cures are genuine in that a change, often dramatic, takes place in the afflicted one. It is not the cure of the illness that should be questioned but the cause of the illness.

Miracles often occur when the individual no longer needs the symptoms. A woman who had suffered from painful rheumatism was, in her words, "miraculously cured" by a series of visits to a healing shrine. In reality, she was cured when her alcoholic husband stopped drinking and resumed a normal home life.

Miracles sometimes can achieve what medical science can't, but they are usually based on an overwhelming desire to believe and a conviction that a cure is possible.

However, cures which are miraculous may not be permanent; the illness may reappear in a different form. A man cured, through faith, of a supposedly crippled foot may develop stomach cramps if the cause of his psychosomatic illness is not removed from his life.

"Now You Are Getting Sleepy!"

Like the pendulum often used to induce a state of hypnosis, the uses of hypnotism swing between two points of interest on the part of the general public. At one end, is its use as a kind of vaudeville act; at the other end, as an aid in medicine.

Hypnosis proves the power of the mind over the body, for hypnotic suggestions to the subject will have physical results. A subject told that his leg is broken will actually feel pain and be unable to use that leg. By the same token, a subject suffering from incapacitating leg pains can recover from these pains under hypnosis. This "cure" may not last, however, for hypnosis is not a treatment but only a process of discovery and suggestion.

Hypnotism is one way of getting beyond the barriers people erect between their "real" selves and their "public" selves. But the use of hypnosis lacks the safety of dealing more directly with the unconscious as is done in psychoanalysis.

Proof that an illness is psychosomatic can be obtained through hypnosis, and symptoms of such an illness can be modified or made to disappear. However, the lasting effect of such changes must in the long run depend on more than hypnosis.

Hypnosis is applied from the outside and therefore is limiting in its effect. Psychosomatic illnesses demand insight from patients before any permanent cure can be accomplished.

Psychosomatic Ills versus Hypochondriasis

In simple terms, someone with a psychosomatic illness says "I feel sick;" a hypochondriac says "I *think* I feel sick."

Hypochondriasis is a neurotic preoccupation with personal health. It is an attention-getting device.

A woman patient who was a hypochondriac complained of persistent insomnia because of worry over a teenage daughter.

"If I get to sleep fifteen minutes a night, I consider myself fortunate," she declared.

She was sincere, but she was obviously not suffering from any of the usual effects of prolonged sleeplessness.

Her embarrassed husband confirmed our supposition. He said his wife did sleep most of the night. She had convinced herself, however, that she did not sleep. In this way she bolstered and maintained her image of herself as a concerned mother.

In general, hypochondriasis is expressed in the *idea* of symptoms rather than in actual symptoms. Fear of disease or illness is a part of the hypochrondriacal attitude. The person who has a psychosomatic illness *exhibits* the symptoms of the disease.

"I have a bad heart," says Mr. A., a hypochondriac. Yet he does not suffer any incapacitating effects from his supposed heart condition. He carries out all of his normal activities while using his "heart condition" as an easy way to get some extra attention and concern from his family and friends. A physical examination of Mr. A. will disclose no changes in his breathing, blood pressure, or organic structure.

"I have a bad heart," says Mr. B., who suffers from psychosomatic illnesses. Mr. B. has shortness of breath, high blood pressure, an irregular heartbeat, and severe chest pains. He is unable to engage in his usual work or other activities. Mr. B. has become an invalid.

Neither Mr. A. nor Mr. B. has actual heart disease, but both use heart trouble as a screen for other problems. Mr. A.'s heart trouble is relatively harmless and could be characterized as a nuisance. Mr. B., however, needs professional help to discover the real reasons for his heart condition. With the proper treatment, he can be restored as a functioning member of society.

The hypochondrical individual is saying "Look at me; if you can't love me, at least feel sorry for me!" The individual with psychosomatic illnesses is often saying "Nobody loves me!"

Psychosomatic ills can be cured by treatment, but hypochondriacal ills are rarely given up by sufferers. They prefer to keep them as part of their personalities. They refuse to admit that their illness does not exist, since to do so would be to lessen their own self-importance.

Hypochondriacs willingly seek medical advice. Being a patient becomes a profession with them. They enjoy reading and hearing about medical matters. Frequently, they build up extensive knowledge—sometimes false—about medicine, diseases, and related subjects. They collect symptoms the way some people collect stamps: A rare one is as much a prize to them as a rare stamp to the stamp collector.

The hypochondriac has a childish concern with himself which is different from the psychosomatic sufferer's inability to adjust to his tensions or find solutions for his problems.

Finally, in hypochondriasis, the patient feels that he knows all the answers. In psychosomatic illnesses, the patient does not.

Ten Danger Signals of Emotional Problems That Lie Behind Psychosomatic Symptoms

Your psychosomatic symptoms may be indicative of emotional problems. They are danger signals telling you that something is wrong.

These signals, all of which represent deviations from normal attitudes, behavior, or health patterns, are:

1. Feelings of anxiety
2. Restlessness
3. Inability to make decisions
4. Irritableness
5. Feelings of sadness
6. Insomnia
7. Loss of appetite
8. Compulsive overeating
9. Fatigue
10. Loss of interest in work, life, or surroundings

If you have a psychosomatic illness, you may have several of these symptoms.

Anxiety is a result of unrelieved tension. You suffer from fear, uncertainty, and feelings of insecurity.

This anxiety is often translated into body functions. The affected individual may become dizzy, tremble, have difficulty breathing, and have attacks of diarrhea or vomiting.

"I feel like my heart is going to stop," explained one patient.

Anxiety produces a painful state of panic.

Restlessness and the inability to make decisions are all further expressions of anxiety.

"I can't sit still when I have an anxiety attack," another patient said. "I have to do something, so I usually scrub the floor!"

Until she was cured of her anxiety, this woman had the cleanest floors in town!

The inability to make decisions can be a serious one in terms of everyday living. Since many decisions are made automatically, a breakdown of this decision-making system results in chaos in your life.

Irritableness is a form of mental restlessness that rapidly uses up your energy. It has an adverse effect upon your personality and all of your personal relationships.

Feelings of sadness and insomnia are distress signals. Often, sadness has no apparent cause. Yet it is there, and its effects, like the effects of insomnia, are seen in physical disorders of the body.

Loss of appetite and overeating are opposite sides of the same coin. They are both self-destructive impulses. They are both attempts to deal with problems in a primitive way.

Fatigue is one of the most common psychosomatic complaints. It is vague in origin but very general in its effect. Since nearly everybody gets tired, fatigue is understandable. It elicits sympathy from others. It can also cover up a multitude of other complaints.

Finally, a loss of interest in outward objects usually signifies an inward conflict.

How to Find Out if Your Symptoms Are Psychosomatic, and What to Do About It

If there is a question in your mind about whether or not your symptoms are psychosomatic, you can find out the answer.

Consult a physician to determine if your symptoms are the symptoms of an organic disease or illness. You cannot decide that for yourself.

However, you may answer some questions about your symptoms which will give you and your doctor clues about your state of health.

Ask yourself what your mental and emotional state was at the onset of your symptoms. Were you unusually upset over anything?

Do your symptoms of illness coincide with times of stress? For example, do you feel better at home than you do at work, or vice versa? A patient I once treated developed progressively more severe symptoms when she spent long periods of time at home. She was unable to eat, complaining of stomach cramps and vomiting. Yet the same woman could take extended trips and not have a sick moment.

Are your symptoms inconsistent? That is, do they fluctuate in intensity without apparent reason? Frequently, a patient with psychosomatic fatigue will still have sufficient energy to do something that is particularly important to him.

Discovering the causes of your psychosomatic symptoms means being willing to discover yourself. It means facing your personality problems. It means solving your problems. It means giving up guilt, frustration, tension, and anxiety along with your poor health.

It also means exchanging those things for new energy, happiness, increased awareness, more creativity, and good health.

III

The Uncommonly Common
Cold

The Commonness of Colds

The ubiquitous cold is rightly named "common," for it is very ordinary and very prevalent among people of all classes and ages. It might be said that the cold is a common denominator that can bring diverse kinds of people to one level. Affairs of state have had to wait because leading statesmen have gotten severe colds. Love affairs have been interrupted, social affairs have been postponed, and careers have been temporarily sidelined because of colds. Colds are indeed the most widespread of all the everyday illnesses.

A cold involves the upper respiratory tract and may be caused by any one of twenty different viruses. It is easy to spot a cold victim by such outward symptoms as sneezing, coughing, running nose, stuffed head, and a debilitating lack of energy.

The cold ranks as a minor disease, yet as any cold-sufferer knows it is major to him. Colds can be disabling. People frequently complain that they can't think clearly with a cold. The constant nose-blowing or coughing interferes with their ability to do and enjoy things. Usually, they lose their interest in food. Most cold-sufferers feel that they present an unattractive picture to others with their red noses, runny eyes, and flushed faces.

Yes, colds are common, and colds are contagious. But there is another side to the picture, and that is the emotional or psychological *predisposition* to colds.

Who Catches Colds?

Anyone, as we have said, can get a cold, but some people have a history of frequent colds. For them there is no "off season" when they can enjoy a respite.

People who constantly catch cold may certainly have a physical problem, but more frequently they have an emotional problem. They catch cold because they need to have some ailment to provide them with a temporary relief from their conflicts. Colds, while creating stress situations of their own, may be preferable to other forms of stress.

Philip N. had been turned down by the girl he wanted to marry. Philip felt, in his words, "like killing myself." Instead he developed a bad cold, and this cold kept Philip emotionally and physically occupied. The cold formed an acceptable stress situation which he could handle. By the time his cold was better, he had had time to develop a more rational view of his unrequited love.

Any individual who is suffering from some emotional stress is a likely candidate for a cold. He may not be aware of it, but he frequently invites a cold by some of his behavior patterns. Because of stress, he may have lowered his resistance with poor eating, lack of sufficient rest, exposure to adverse weather conditions, or failure to wear adequate clothing. In addition, his mental state may be so negative that he unconsciously wishes for some sickness. And since colds are contagious and common, they are the easiest sickness to get.

There is a secondary gain from a cold: it may lead to a period of "mothering." Frequently, the individual unconsciously desires to be pampered and cared for by others. This primitive infantile reaction to separation anxiety may have actually caused the cold. The cold-sufferer manipulates other people and his environment so that he becomes the center of concern and attention. The whole concept of secondary gain will be explained in greater detail in Chapter IV.

I do want to make it clear, however, that a cold is a very real ailment. Colds are of concern in psychosomatic medicine from the standpoint of an individual's susceptibility to them.

Some Startling Facts about Colds

Every year hundreds of millions of dollars are spent on cold remedies. Far more money is lost by workers who either cannot report for work or are not able to work effectively because of colds. The wage-loss figure is estimated at between $5 and $15 billion.

Although there is no known medical curative for colds, countless remedies are available commercially. Colds are expensive for the cold-sufferer. Recent surveys estimate that more than $500 million is spent annually for cold remedies. The sale of decongestants, nasal sprays, cough medicines, nose drops, lozenges, and salves has continued to increase. Some of these medicines are dispensed by prescription, but the greater number are available over the counter.

Cold and cough remedies account for a high proportion of magazine, newspaper, radio, and television advertising. In addition, twenty-five percent of the advertising that supports medical journals is derived from patent cold remedies. These remedies promise relief from irritating cold symptoms, and in most cases they do help alleviate the unpleasantness of colds. However, they treat only the symptoms, the outward signs; they do nothing about the causes.

No one can really afford the luxury of having a cold. The best preventative is not some pill or magic remedy (such as the old folk-remedy of a bag of garlic or asafetida worn around the neck) or the new emphasis on vitamins, especially Vitamin C. These things are of little use if the individual's emotional attitude is setting the stage for some illness or accident.

Suggestibility and Colds

Suggestibility works two ways. A person may believe that he is particularly susceptible and thus he may anticipate that he is going to get a cold. In a sense, he looks forward to a series of colds.

On the other hand, suggestibility can also play an important part in keeping people from catching cold. Having an important job to do or an appointment to keep may prevent a person from getting a cold. One woman told me that she had not had a cold the entire year she had worked at a new job where first-year sick leave was limited. "Almost as

soon as my probationary period was up," she said, "I
caught a bad cold."

As mentioned in Chapter I, the validity and success of
any cure is largely dependent upon the patient's attitude.
The most worthless "cure" can work if the individual is suffering from a psychosomatic illness and has faith in the
cure. This is suggestibility in action!

The popularity of cold remedies and so-called preventatives lies in the willingness to believe in their efficacy. Most
of these remedies can offer some form of temporary relief,
and the preventatives have the advantage of making you believe in your own immunity to colds. Again, however, I
want to stress that most cold remedies take care of the
symptoms. They do not keep you from catching cold again,
nor do they uncover the real cause of your cold. This is not
to imply that you should not bother to treat your cold
symptoms; you should, but you should also try to discover
the cause of your cold.

Laura B. had frequent colds. She had tried many remedies, and although they gave her relief, she was not "cured."
As a result of her many colds, she felt tired and unable to
carry out her normal activities. Psychiatric treatment revealed that Laura had a personality problem that was really
responsible for her colds.

As a child, Laura had been overly protected and babied
by her widowed mother. Told that she was delicate and un-
well, Laura was encouraged to think of herself in terms of
illness. Her mother was especially concerned about colds.
She herself had frequent colds and taught Laura to expect
to have colds. As a result, even in adulthood, Laura regarded herself as being in poor health and particularly susceptible to colds.

By contrast, Irene T. did not have colds. Asked what
her "secret" of immunity was, Irene's revealing reply was,
"I haven't time for a cold!"

If you are troubled by frequent colds, you may be in-
fluenced by negative suggestion. It is just as easy to tell
yourself that you are *not* going to catch a cold as it is to ex-

pect to have one. The idea is to change your susceptibility orientation from negative to positive. Tell yourself, as Irene did, "I haven't time for a cold!" It is one of the best immunization techniques ever devised.

Colds are not as contagious as we have been led to believe. What are more contagious are attitudes about colds. A friend gave this interesting example of colds and suggestibility.

"I had lunch with a relative," she said, "and when I met her at the restaurant, the first thing she said to me was that she had a very bad cold and was afraid I might catch it from her. Throughout the entire meal, she made many references to her sore throat, fever, feelings of discomfort, and other symptoms, and each time she did she repeated that she hoped I wouldn't get a cold, too. By the time the meal was finished, I began to think it possible that I might catch her cold, and on the way home I thought my throat was starting to get sore. When I sneezed a couple of times, I was sure that I had started to get a cold. As I reached into my medicine cabinet for a cold tablet, I suddenly realized that my cousin had talked me into believing that I was going to be ill. Telling myself that I was making myself get a cold by following her suggestion, I put the tablet back, went out into the garden, and did some weeding. I forgot about my cold symptoms, and when I came in, they had disappeared."

Separation Anxiety and Colds

Body-chatter, as we mentioned in Chapter I, is a way of expressing hidden fears, anxieties, guilts, worries, and other emotional problems. The body-chatter of colds performs the same function—it is trying to tell you that something is wrong. There is a hidden meaning to that runny nose, that cough or sore throat. You have to discover the meaning of this form of body-chatter.

In terms of language, we might relate this body chatter to the phrase "out in the cold"—we may have gotten the cold because we feel some sense of emotional isolation from others. Any degree of real or imagined rejection by others can develop into a state of separation anxiety.

Separation anxiety is tension that develops in an individual as a result of his being or feeling separated from the person or persons he loves.

Separation anxiety starts in infancy. The primary person to whom we are attached is our mother. A small baby may cry when his mother removes herself from his immediate consciousness. Babies have been observed to sneeze when their mothers leave the room. This is a body-chatter response to separation anxiety.

Infants do not see very well, and much of their identification process is through a sense of smell. This acute sense of smell helps the infant to recognize and relate to his mother. It also makes the baby aware of his mother's emotional state and changes of state, since emotion produces chemical changes in perspiration. The baby can therefore smell a change or variation even if he is not aware of what has happened. For example, a mother may have a fight with her husband and then go into the baby's room to feed him. As soon as she picks the baby up, he begins to cry. The mother believes that the baby is aware that a quarrel has taken place although this would be impossible for a small baby to comprehend. What has happened is that the baby smells the change in the mother's body odor. This change frightens the baby, and he cries because he does not recognize his own mother.

A similar situation can occur when the mother gets dressed to go out for the evening and puts on perfume. Just before leaving, she goes in to see the baby, who again does not recognize her because of the perfume. When the baby sneezes or cries, the mother's response may be to say, "See, he knows we're going out, and he doesn't want me to go!" Or she may say in alarm, "We can't go. The baby is catching a cold and I'd better stay home and look after him!"

This situation provides the mother with a false ego-trip since she feels that she is so needed by her baby. And the baby who is crying or sneezing is really suffering from separation anxiety.

Chapter V will cover in more detail some of the emotional problems associated with the nose and the sense of smell. The nose, like any other part of the body, can talk back in psychosomatic terms.

Separation anxiety persists into later childhood and adulthood. It is a primitive reaction, which is different from the feeling of sadness we have when someone we care for goes away. That sadness is a conscious emotion and sense of loss—a minor form of grief. The separation anxiety that adults have is distinct from sadness in that it is almost always unconscious; it is repressed because it is such a primitive emotion, but it may have a serious effect on behavior.

A Case of Latent Separation Anxiety

A patient undergoing psychoanalysis reported a dream in which he was driving down the street and saw his mother standing by the road, asking for a ride. The sight of his mother waiting there upset him. Instead of stopping the car, he passed her by and tried to increase his speed, but the car failed to respond and began to falter. Seeing that he was not going to pick her up, his mother began to scream, run after the car, and throw rocks. In a burst of determination, the patient pushed the accelerator to the floor and got the needed power. He was able to speed away, leaving his mother behind.

In real life this patient had had trouble in dissociating himself from his mother. She had encouraged him to become extremely and increasingly dependent upon her. As a child he had stayed by her side instead of seeking playmates of his own age and interests. In adulthood he was unable to have satisfactory relationships with women, since his mother insisted on being the primary interest in his life.

Finally, in an effort to change his life and achieve a mature emotional outlook, he sought psychiatric treatment. In the middle of telling this very revealing dream, he began to sneeze, and by the end of the session he had the symptoms of a cold. This sneezing was an indication of his repressed separation anxiety. His "cold" lasted twenty-four hours, and during that period he felt very sad. Although he knew that his relationship with his mother was not a good one, he nevertheless had a depression associated with the idea that he would have to make a break with her. His cold was a primitive body reaction to that particular stress situation. But once he had decided and had become emotionally reconciled to the fact that he would, as in the dream, have to leave his mother behind, his cold disappeared. It no longer had a psychological purpose in his life.

The Unconscious and Repression

The unconscious is that part of the mind which is the repository of all primitive feelings and memories. Repressed memories and impulses are also kept there, and although they *influence* conduct, they usually remain repressed. You are not often aware of these influences from the unconscious, and at times you may even be puzzled as to why you are behaving in a certain way. The comedian who gets a laugh from the audience by saying of an action, "The Devil made me do it" would be closer to the truth if he said, "My unconscious made me do it."

Repression is also the way in which we block out unpleasant or painful memories. When we repress these memories, we are denying their existence. Sometimes, however, a memory is so strong that it continues to rise to the surface of our consciousness. If we are determined to repress it, we will try other means, such as rationalization or keeping it buried in the unconscious.

Lee F. was being treated by his family physician for various psychosomatic ills. He appeared to be a healthy man, although he complained of vague symptoms of pain and general feelings of depression and fatigue. He reached the point where it was difficult for him to eat.

His doctor suggested that Lee consult me to discover

the real cause of his poor health, since it was obvious after tests that there was no organic cause. After a period of treatment, the cause of Lee's health problems was revealed. They came from his attempt to repress through rationalization an action he had taken.

A few months before he became ill, Lee had stolen some money from the firm where he worked. Taking the money was wrong according to Lee's moral standards, but he tried to repress those standards as well as the memory of his theft. When he could not keep the memory buried, he tried to rationalize the theft by calling it a "loan." But his unconscious kept throwing it back until under the tension it caused he developed psychosomatic symptoms. He was still looking for a way out of his moral dilemma.

Depression and Colds

There seems to be a connection between colds and depression. And although most people say that they are depressed because they have colds, in many cases it would be more accurate to say that they have colds because they are depressed.

In 1968 it was reported that Dr. Merl M. Jackel of the Downstate Medical Center of the State University of New York had been studying the relationship between colds and depression. The study was conducted over a three-year period on ten patients who were under psychoanalytic care. The results of his study, reported at a meeting of the American Psychoanalytic Association, showed that there was a definite connection between depression and colds. During the time of the study, Dr. Jackel saw thirty-five colds, twenty-six of which were associated with depression. He also found that his patients who suffered from colds frequently had strong feelings of repressed anger and hostility.

Individuals who are depressed have a general "I don't care" attitude about life. They are *willing* to catch cold, as the discomfort they have from the cold in a sense justifies their feelings of depression and lack of worth.

As one patient put it, "I guess this cold is all I deserve

to get out of life." She had very low self-esteem and no self-confidence. After analysis she began to have some regard for herself as a person, and she no longer needed colds.

The next time you feel depressed, check your state of health. Do your feel that you might be catching cold? Do you *expect* to catch a cold? You should be able to prevent yourself from getting a cold by understanding and controlling your emotions.

Time, Calendars, and Colds

Medical researchers have also discovered that there is a link between time—days or months—and colds. Mondays find more people suffering from colds or incipient colds. This factor can be directly tied to a dislike or resentment of work and work routines.

In Dr. Jackel's study, fourteen colds were reported on Mondays. These depression-associated colds occurred after the patients had been out of touch with the doctor for several days. Seven colds were reported on Fridays, the day before separation for the weekend.

As a psychiatrist, I have observed the same thing in my patients over a period of seventeen years. One woman in particular who had no family or close friends and had become emotionally dependent upon her analytic sessions for human contact, appeared outwardly calm when I announced that I would be away on vacation for the next few weeks. However, she immediately began to exhibit the signs of a cold, signs which were not present at the beginning of her visit.

Few people get colds at the beginning of their own vacations, but there is a high incidence of colds when vacations end. Many people come back to work and complain that although they had a good time, they caught a terrible cold because of the air conditioning, the climate, or for some other reason. The real cause was probably their natural and understandable desire to remain on vacation and not return to work.

One man who was slated to give a speech at a company dinner came down with a bad cold the day before the dinner. Supposedly, he was disappointed at not being able to be present, but he was secretly pleased because he dreaded speaking in public. Another patient always caught cold just before she was to visit relatives.

Esther G. suffered from colds during her menstrual periods. Since she lost several days a month because of her colds, she felt run-down and unable to take part in her usual activities. As analysis revealed, the colds and her menstrual periods were associated, though not in the way she had explained it to herself and others.

Her menstrual periods did not make her so weak that she caught cold. Her mental attitude toward menstruation made her depressed, and her cold was the visible symptom of her tension. This tension resulted from being frightened by her mother into believing that menstruation could cause cancer. Through treatment, Esther learned to recognize the absurdity of her fears and to accept her menstrual periods as a part of normal womanhood. When she was able to do so, she no longer had colds during her periods.

Change and Colds

Closely related to the time and calendar motif in colds is the change factor. Any change in a person's status or situation may cause that person to develop a cold. Many people I have observed develop colds soon after starting new jobs or adding new responsibilities to their present jobs.

"I got this terrible cold right after we moved" is another remark that is frequently heard. The speaker usually attributes it to fatigue, but a more accurate diagnosis is that making a change in living surroundings caused the cold. Any time an individual is separated either temporarily or permanently from anything that could be interpreted as a mother figure, he can get a cold. Thus, leaving home for an extended period, leaving school, a place of employment, or friends and family not only means a change in life, it can also mean a bad cold. Soldiers transferred from one base to another frequently report at their new base with severe colds.

Over a period of six months I talked with three robbery victims, two of whom also admitted having bad colds immediately after they discovered their losses.

Most Colds Are Not Contagious!

It is my conviction that the vast majority of colds are not infectious in nature but are psychosomatic. I would say that the cold is the chief psychosomatic illness of our culture.

There are psychological causes behind the majority of colds, but they are usually overlooked or ignored either deliberately or because of an unfamiliarity with the concept of the cold as a psychosomatic illness.

That colds need not be contagious can be shown by studying families in which colds occur. Where there is a climate of depression or unhappiness, the cold is usually passed along from one member to the other. Where there is a strong feeling of self-esteem and happiness, one member may have a cold but the others usually do not catch it.

We have been conditioned to expect to have colds and to accept them as a bothersome adjunct to life. But we need not suffer from colds. More attention and study should be given their psychological and emotional aspects. If we don't understand colds, it is simply because we don't understand ourselves.

How to Prevent or Limit Colds

You can learn to prevent or at least limit your colds. To do this, you need to become aware of the unconscious thoughts and emotions that can cause you to catch cold.

Your body will give you some important hints which, if you teach yourself to listen to this form of body chatter, can alert you to the possibility of a cold. These clues can warn you and arouse your defenses. They are minor irritations which can turn into major symptoms of discomfort.

Learn to know what those minor symptoms can mean. That sniffling nose can often be translated into a feeling of sadness or grief. Coughing and sneezing may be body-chatter for feelings of unhappiness, guilt, or frustration. That scratchy throat may symbolize an irritation with your work, your spouse, your financial situation, or any other area of tension. Body ache preceding a cold may signify emotional stress.

When you feel these first symptoms of a cold, you should take time to analyze your immediate situation. Check to see if you are suffering some kind of separation anxiety. Take a look at your emotional barometer—is it high or low? If low, what are the reasons and what can you do about them?

Your cold may be a substitute for some emotion that you are trying to repress. For example, a father came down with a bad cold the day of his daughter's wedding; the real reason for his cold was that he felt unhappy over losing his daughter. The cold was a substitute for crying, which he felt would be inappropriate.

Don't Talk Yourself into a Cold

Accepting the premise that colds are usually not contagious means that you also have to be willing to accept the responsibility for determining whether or not you are going to have a cold.

Don't talk yourself into a cold! If you find that you are saying to yourself, "I must be getting a cold," check your motivations. Is there some reason why a cold would be a convenient "out" for you? Are you looking for some way in which to hide from life and the problems of life?

Don't let others talk you into a cold, either. The danger here comes from well-meaning but misguided friends or relatives who may stress the negative or seek to make you dependent. We all carry into adulthood that infantile characteristic of dependency that makes us enjoy being fussed over. There are ways of having that need fulfilled, but having a cold is not one of the better ways.

Finally, don't let radio and television commercials influence you into believing that colds are unavoidable. Many of these commercials also cater to the idea of being mothered; that is, they show a sympathetic wife giving cold medication to her husband and fussing over him. This appeals to the desire to have an understanding wife-mother who will dispense not only cold remedies but affection as well.

If the voice of the "medicine-man announcer" is loud in the land, it is not necessary for you to say Yes to his suggestions. Remind yourself that each time you say Yes to a cold, you are saying No to some creative aspect of your life.

Headaches—The Number One Illness

Headaches Are Number One on the Symptom Parade

If there were a popularity contest on the grounds of frequency of any of the usual symptoms, headaches would win.

In medical practice, headaches are the most common symptom reported to doctors. This is in general medical practice, not in psychiatry.

Yet even in general practice, it is estimated by doctors that nearly ninety percent of these headaches are psychosomatic. They have no physical basis.

"But my headaches are real!" exclaimed a patient when she was told that her headaches were psychosomatic in origin.

Of course they were. Any headache is real in terms of pain, suffering, and discomfort. The severity of the pain and extent of the discomfort varies from mildly to totally disabling.

The Actual and the Hidden Causes of Headaches

The actual cause of a headache can be pressure on, or contraction of, any of the pain-sensitive areas of the head. Thus, headaches can be caused by a change in the pressure of the fluid around the brain.

What interests us here, however, are the hidden causes of headaches. They are responsible for nine out of ten headaches. Hidden causes are as varied as people because they are people-related. Some of the most common causes are tension, stress, fear, guilt, anxiety, frustration, and anger.

That tenth case can be caused by tumors, high blood pressure, glaucoma, sinus infections, or other diseases. For this reason, persistent headaches should be first checked out for organic causes.

Treating a Headache

Treating a headache is a full-time occupation with some people. They use popular modern headache remedies or old-time folk remedies.

The U.S. Public Health Service has estimated that in the United States, more than $400 million are spent each year on headache remedies.

Although aspirin continues to be the most popular and effective pain-reliever for headaches, there are over two hundred pain-relief products on the market.

Seven out of ten adults use some kind of a headache remedy once or twice a month. Some people take headache remedies as a precautionary measure.

"I always take an aspirin before I go downtown to shop," a friend told me. "I'm afraid I'll get a headache if I don't."

Another woman regularly took two aspirin tablets when she got up each morning to prevent headaches. Unfortunately, her plan didn't always work, for in times of real stress she suffered from severe migraine headaches.

Pills and other remedies can offer only a temporary relief of pain. They do not remove the hidden causes. They do not solve the underlying problems.

Why the Head Is Affected by Psychosomatic Responses

Why is it specifically the head that is so often affected by psychosomatic responses?

The head is considered to be the seat of the intellect. From the head are issued thoughts, desires, and directions. It is the command post of our bodies.

When an individual uses his intellect as an emotional weapon to get what he thinks he wants, he may become uneasy with some of the results. And the drives which originate at this command post may not please him—indeed at times they may shock him.

Occasional anger at a parent, with an unexpressed desire to kill that parent, is a normal reaction in childhood. Nonetheless it is a feeling that can be frightening because it demands punishment. But the child only gradually becomes aware of his anger thoughts and learns that they are considered wicked. The adult, on the other hand, is very much aware of his thoughts, so that when he becomes angry enough at someone to feel the urge to kill, he also feels a sense of guilt. Since the desire is unexpressed and hidden, the thinker must punish himself. By having a headache, he punishes his head where the "evil" thought originated. The severity of the headache will be related to the degree of guilt that is felt.

How Success Gave Joe a Headache

Joe was the owner of a large and successful grocery store, but he was finding it more and more difficult to attend to his business.

"These terrible headaches I get, Doctor, just keep me from doing anything. Sometimes I can't even get out of bed and go down to the store," he explained.

Psychoanalysis revealed that Joe's headaches were associated with his success in business.

Joe had taken over the operation of the store from his father, who wanted to retire. His father had not been a progressive businessman but had been content to make a fair living from the store.

Joe, who had studied business administration in college, instituted new procedures and streamlined the business. His father interpreted the changes Joe made and the resulting increase in business and profits as a criticism of the way he himself had run the store. Soon he was making Joe feel guilty for his success.

Joe was too well trained to fail, but he could punish himself for succeeding. Since he had surpassed his father because of his superior education, Joe punished his brain by having headaches.

When he understood his father's resentment and his own subsequent feelings of guilt, Joe was cured of his headaches.

The Ego, the Id, and the Superego

In psychiatric terms we think of the brain as being divided into three parts. This is not an anatomical division but a psychological division. These three divisions are called the ego, the id, and the superego.

The ego is the conscious part of the brain. It acts as the mediator between your internal drives and the external world. In other words, the ego is a go-between and arbiter.

The id is part of the unconscious. It is the pleasure- and destruction-seeking area of the mind. Your inner drives and impulses come from your id. These include your sexual and aggressive drives.

Your superego is also part of your unconscious. Here you will find your ego-ideal and guilt systems. Your superego is your "right and wrong" system, or in a familiar word, your conscience.

Conflict or Compromise

There can be conflict between the ego and the id when drives or impulses do not fit in with reality. There can also be conflict between the ego and the superego.

This conflict between the various parts of the mind is called *inter-psychic tension*. The conflict is in the mind; the tension is felt in the body.

Headaches are one manifestation of inter-psychic tension.

You have to choose between conflict and compromise. Your ego has to compromise your drives with the demands and rules of the exterior world. If it can't do this, you will have to suffer from the effects of conflict.

"My Conscience Gave Me a Headache"

"I guess my conscience gave me a headache," said young Ralph in explaining why he had not been with a group of his friends who had been arrested for smoking marijuana.

"I was with them when they started, but just before the joint was passed to me, I got this terrific pain in my head and I felt dizzy. I was afraid I was going to be sick, so I left and went home. I felt better after I was home awhile."

Undoubtedly it was his "conscience" which had prompted Ralph's headache. On the one hand, Ralph wanted to be one of the gang and do what his friends did, but he also was very much aware of his parents' disapproval of drugs.

When he was unable to say No to his friends, a conflict was set up and he developed a sudden headache.

"Don't Mess with My Head!"

A common hip expression is "Don't mess with my head!" By using this expression, people show an understanding of how conflict is caused when there are differences between ideals and actions and between opposing ideas.

People direct this remark particularly toward those whom they feel are trying to confuse them or brainwash them. It is often directed toward politicians, sociologists, and others in authority.

It is true that many people do try to "mess with our heads" in this respect, but most of us rarely object overtly. Instead, we get headaches or other psychosomatic illnesses.

The woman who says, "I don't know anyting about politics; in fact, politicians give me a headache!" is telling the truth. So is the man who reports glumly, "World affairs give me a pain in the neck!"

The Power of Headaches

It is not unusual to hear a person say, "When my head aches, I ache all over!"

Headaches are frequently accompanied by nausea and dizziness. This is especially true for headaches caused by guilt feelings. The effects of these self-punitive headaches tend to radiate throughout the entire body. A person with psychosomatic headaches is predisposed to spreading his symptoms to other parts of his body.

Cervantes in *Don Quixote* said, "When the head aches, all the members partake of the pains."

When Things Start Spinning

Vertigo or dizziness can happen to anyone, but it does happen to some people with alarming frequency. When there is no organic basis for this vertigo, we can safely assume that it is psychosomatic.

Dizziness is a common psychosomatic reaction to conflict, stress, and tension. It may be accompanied by headache and ringing in the ears.

Headache pain may be almost unbearable, but dizziness is frightening. Victims feel as if they are losing touch with the world around them, as indeed they are.

Vertigo is the result of a destructive impulse. It is called forth by feelings of guilt and is a form of self-punishment.

The feeling one gets from vertigo can be compared with the sensation of being shaken. In fact, one patient who suffered from dizzy spells whenever she became angry or upset, remembered that her mother had always punished her by shaking her. Now she was punishing herself by a close approximation of the same method.

Some cases of dizziness can be traced back to a fear of falling. Other fears may be added to this, so that as an adult an individual may react to any fear or stress situation by becoming dizzy.

A patient who suffered from such a condition said his first memory was of learning to walk and of falling down in the process. "Once," he said, "I fell and hit my head on the edge of a rocker. I must have cut myself because I remember blood running down my face and I remember crying."

He went on to say that his mother scolded him rather than comforted him when he fell. Thus, he developed a secondary anxiety in which the fear of displeasing his mother was added to his fear of falling. These fears were carried into his adult life; he became dizzy when stress or conflict occurred in either his home or work situations.

Clues to causes of dizziness may often be found in dreams. Many persons suffering from vertigo report having recurrent dreams of falling. They dream of being in elevators, often faulty, and on heights. They sometimes dream of being in automobiles or trains which are going too fast for safety.

There is often a certain amount of unconscious shame connected with dizziness. This may be because dizziness symbolizes a loss of self-control. Thus we have the derogatory term "dizzy," as in "He's a dizzy person."

Fainting as a Defense Mechanism

"Fainting isn't really much fun," said a patient who was subject to fainting spells.

She knew that technically fainting was caused by a drop in her blood pressure, but she didn't know what caused that drop. Analysis showed that fear was responsible. She had been brought up in a home where her father, an alcoholic, had frequently beaten her. As an adolescent she had developed fainting spells whenever there was a conflict between her and her father. He stopped beating her at about this time apparently because her fainting frightened him.

She continued to faint, however, whenever she was in the presence of actual or possible situations of conflict. When there was any unpleasantness with her husband she fainted, and because her husband did not understand her background, he accused her of deliberately doing this to annoy him.

Treatment helped her to overcome her fear of conflict. She learned to discuss disagreements with her husband instead of fainting to avoid them.

When fainting is psychosomatic, it is a defense mechanism. Faced with an unpleasant situation, you need a way of protecting yourself from your feelings of anxiety or guilt. You sense an impending loss of self-esteem.

Running away from the situation might seem an ideal response and solution. But if you can't run away physically, you run away mentally and emotionally by fainting. The hope is that when you revive from your fainting spell, the situation will be changed.

Fainting is an attempt to escape from reality, whether the reality is bad news which you don't want to accept as true, conflict with another person, or a task you don't feel capable of performing. In fainting, you are literally "hiding out" within yourself.

Is That Hangover Necessary?

The hangover is a well-known and socially-accepted reaction, but is it really necessary?

We generally associate hangovers with alcohol, but the symptoms of a hangover can be associated with any kind of overindulgence. Overeating can give you as miserable a morning-after as overdrinking can.

Guilt is an ingredient in any hangover. The greater the degree of guilt, the more the victim will suffer.

This explains why sometimes the hangover is disproportionate to the actual amount of alcohol consumed.

"I don't understand why I have such a hangover," Mr. A. groaned. "I only had two drinks last night. I usually drink much more than that, but I have never felt this bad!"

Investigation revealed that Mr. A. was really suffering from guilt.

"I should have stayed home and worked on my company report," he said, "but when some friends invited me out, I just forgot about it."

A similar reaction was that of a woman who suffered all the classic symptoms of a classic hangover after only one drink whenever she went out socially and left her invalid mother at home.

Headaches as a Reflection of Childhood Frustration

Headaches are often the result of an accumulation of frustrations left over from childhood. These may include a repressed destructive impulse toward the mother.

When we become adults, we frequently push to the backs of our minds those memories of our dependency days. But if your childhood dependency needs were not adequately met you may still feel frustrated as an adult. That frustration is an accumulation of all childhood pain at not having needs met, and it may appear in the form of headaches.

Why headaches? In some cases, the people who suffer from them were often punished during childhood by being struck on the head. Others may have repressed childhood fantasies in which they relieved their rage by hitting the mother in the head and killing her. Their adult headaches reflect the same repressed rage, accompanied by an automatic self-punishment for the rage.

Unsatisfied dependency needs and anger at one's mother may be transferred to one's wife. This unconscious process is known as *transference* and involves the transferring of childhood emotions to people who were not the original recipients of those emotions.

Mr. B. becomes violently angry with his wife if he doesn't like what she serves for dinner of if she burns any of the food. He is really still angry with his mother, who used to force him to eat what she thought he should eat, not what he wanted to eat. He had also been forced to eat what had been prepared, even if it was overcooked or burned.

"You Give Me a Headache!"

Another reason that headaches are a popular form of psychosomatic reaction is that children are often exposed to headaches as a form of household illness.

Children, who are frequently more astute than adults like to believe them to be, can see that adults often use headaches to mask their true feelings.

"No, we can't go, because I have a headache," "You give me a headache," and "Be quiet because I have a headache" are all phrases that do not really fool a child but do build up resentments.

They also provide a pattern of behavior that the child can carry over and use in his own adult life so that he, in turn, adopts headaches as his own way of reacting to stress situations.

Mr. C., whose mother used to say, "Stop, you're giving me a headache!" whenever he wanted attention, now uses those same words to his wife whenever she asks him to do something around the house.

Headaches and the Primal Scene

Another set of dynamics behind headaches are fantasies of the primal scene.

Primal scene refers to an individual's recollection of his first observation of the sex act. This may even be an imagined "scene" which was suggested by sounds overheard or remarks made by others. Or it may be based upon observing the sexual behavior of animals.

When actual observation does occur, it may involve witnessing intercourse between the child's parents. It can also be the witnessing of a seduction.

A person's recollection of such events, his primal scene, often produces psychosomatic symptoms.

Since a child cannot always logically interpret what he sees, he may interpret sexual intercourse between his parents as an act of aggression and violence. When the child becomes an adult he may have headaches whenever he comes into sexual contact with a member of the opposite sex. Such contact may be overt or conduct of a seductive nature.

Headaches are frequently associated with the primal scene because the child sees kissing and biting in sex play as activities involving the head. In addition, the child watches the scene with his eyes or hears it with his ears, and of course the eyes and ears are sense organs in his head.

The combination of feelings experienced by the child is guilt for watching, plus a sense of loss at being excluded from the activity.

Every psychosomatic symptom is precipitated by some current event. The nature of the current event frequently reveals what the unconscious childhood conflicts are.

One patient suffered from severe headaches, but only on Sundays. Analysis revealed that as a child he saw his parents having intercourse on Sundays when his father was home from work.

Migraine Headaches

Migraine headaches are no different from other headaches except that they are more severe. A migraine headache is more persistent and often temporarily disabling. It is often called "sick" headache, since it is frequently accompanied by nausea, vomiting, constipation or diarrhea, and an inability to use the eyes.

The causes of migraine are the same as the causes of other headaches.

Carol began to suffer migraine headaches in her senior year in high school because she was afraid she would not get the high grades her parents insisted upon.

Tom, a college student, was pushed into having migraine headaches by his mother, who criticized his interest in girls. She accused him of being interested only in sex, and once said in an argument with him, "You're so crazy about girls, you have a prick in your head!" Soon after that episode, Tom's migraine headaches began.

The "migraine personality" is often extremely tense, nervous, meticulous, and sensitive to criticism. Such an individual may have many repressed emotions. He may set too high standards for himself or accept too high standards from his parents or others in positions of authority.

Headaches as a Psychosomatic Equivalent

Frequently, headaches are a psychosomatic equivalent. The psychosomatic victim expresses his conflicts through his headaches.

If he consults a psychiatrist he may, as other people do, refer to his doctor as a "head shrinker," a popular slang term.

These words can have a special meaning for the headache sufferer, for he often complains that his head feels as if it is swollen. This feeling is natural, since all of his attention is concentrated on the pain in his head.

In addition, a "head shrinker" can also be interpreted as the person who is able to shrink those aggressive drives and impulses by bringing them out into the open through treatment.

Headaches and Traumatic Memories

Some headaches will appear in connection with remembering a traumatic event. Thus, in psychiatric treatment, just before an old traumatic memory is going to be revealed, the patient develops a severe headache. This old memory may also be revealed in dreams, fantasies, or associations. Such memories figuratively and literally give the patient a headache.

One man suffered from headaches whenever he visited his sister. He blamed it on the change in climate. Analysis revealed that he had these headaches because of early masturbatory practices with his sister.

A woman patient was unable to attend church services because of severe headaches. Analysis revealed an old traumatic memory dating from her adolescence. At that time a church organist had made sexual remarks and suggestions when she had gone alone to the church to practice for a solo. She subsequently became ill with what was diagnosed as "severe migraine."

For years she had avoided church services whenever

she could, saying that crowds made her nervous and brought on her headaches. Yet she could attend other types of crowded functions.

Auditory Symptoms in Headaches

Many headache victims also complain of auditory symptoms such as ringing or buzzing in the ears. These auditory disturbances can sometimes be traced to the primal scene, when the child overheard sounds which he related to sexual intercourse.

One patient had had rape fantasies as a child in which she imagined an intruder coming in through her window, striking her on the head, and assaulting her sexually. She later developed headaches with auditory symptoms whenever she was attracted to a possible sexual partner.

Her primal scene was a recollection based on sounds she had overheard outside her parents' bedroom. She had interpreted sexual intercourse from these sounds to be an act of violence and brutality. In fact, she remembered hearing her mother cry out on one occasion, "Stop, you're hurting me!"

My patient's headaches were also punitive in nature, combining excitement and self-punishment for her sexual fantasies.

You Can Help Your Headaches

Headaches can be helped. You can help your headaches.

Look for the psychomatic trigger that starts your headaches. See if you can make changes in your life that eliminate the triggering situation. Bring your repressed memories and fantasies to the surface. When you understand them, they lose their power over your actions.

If you are overly active slow down and look for ways in which you can relax.

Decide if you are using headaches as a cover-up or a

convenience. Look behind your headaches and find your real reasons for taking refuge in them.

You can control or avoid headaches by eliminating the tyranny of tension from your life. Handle worries, fears, and other emotional problems with logic and realistic thinking.

Remember, if you can think your way into a headache, you can also think your way out of a headache!

IV

The Psychological Significance of Gastrointestinal Disorders

Your Gastrointestinal Barometer

One of the most effective and constant barometers of your emotions and of personality changes is your gastrointestinal system. Happiness, tension, depression, excitement, and a myriad of other emotions are all expressed through some phase of that system.

The mouth, stomach, and bowels are intimately affected by what and how you think and feel. When nervous, you may appear calm to others, but you are usually very much aware of that uncomfortable "churning" feeling in your stomach.

Digestive-tract disorders are not only caused by some organic diseases, but a large percentage are caused by emotional disturbances. Eating and elimination processes can and are affected by psychosomatic illnesses.

Nervous indigestion, nervous stomach, colitis, ulcers, anorexia nervosa, diarrhea, and obesity share a common element—psychic problems. They also share the common qualities of disrupting the lives of the afflicted persons and contributing to personality conflicts.

The Oral Stage of Development

The oral stage is the earliest stage of human development. We first relate to the world in an oral way, through our mouths. As infants we are interested only in sucking and feeding. Therefore, the person of prime importance is our mother or the person who feeds us regularly.

This oral stage lasts from birth to eighteen or nineteen months, when interests normally shift to the anal stage of development.

Many of your own personality traits as well as your personality problems can be traced back to the oral stage. If this period is one of frustration and conflict, the effects will show in childhood as well as adulthood.

The oral stage has two predominant phases—the sucking phase and the biting phase. Sucking starts at birth and is the infant's main interest for the first eight or nine months. Biting starts at the end of the sucking phase and usually lasts until the eighteenth month. However, it is not unusual to have remnants of both sucking and biting persist beyond these so-called normal periods.

The period of oral sucking is one of need and extreme dependence. In the oral biting stage hostility, aggression, and insecurity first appear. It is also the first tentative step toward personality independence.

Continual frustration in the oral stage of development can result in a permanent fixation at this level. Since adults obviously cannot continue to suck at a bottle or breast—or to bite people—they have to find and use socially acceptable substitutes.

The Adult Oral Character

We say that a person has an oral character when he shows evidence of having remained emotionally at the oral stage of development.

The individual who is fixated on that first eight months of development will get pleasure out of smoking or sucking on a pipe or pencil. He was a chronic thumbsucker as a child and may still get pleasure from his thumb or fingers, but in a less obvious way. That is, he may put his index finger in his mouth while thinking, or keep his thumb pressed against his lips.

The oral biting stage shows up in adulthood in habits of nail biting, chewing on pencils or other objects, and even in attitudes of sarcasm. We usually say that such a person makes "biting" remarks.

The oral character is particularly concerned with food. He may be a fussy eater or a food faddist. More often, the oral person feels unfulfilled and unsatisfied and becomes a compulsive eater.

In general, the oral character is still infantile in his responses to life. Emotionally immature, he often lacks self-confidence and self-assurance. As a result of his oral fixation, he may suffer from various psychosomatic illnesses, all related to the mouth or to eating.

Obesity and Kinds of Hunger

We all recognize obesity and know that its immediate cause is overeating. But obesity is most often a psychosomatic illness; it is a psychophysiologic disorder that is gastrointestinal in nature. The obese person usually has a compulsion to eat.

Many overweight people attempt to excuse their fatness on the grounds that they are victims of glandular imbalance or that they need to consume large quantities of food in order to "keep their strength up." Scientists have found, however, that no more than five percent of overweight cases are caused by some physical disability such as glandular deficiency. The remaining percentage are overweight because of emotional problems or inappropriate behavior patterns. In some cases these behavior patterns have been set by parents who insisted that healthy children are fat children. It has been found to be very difficult for adults to cut down on their food consumption if they were encouraged to form habits of overeating when they were children.

Too much food and too much of the wrong kinds of food are the *apparent* hungers that cause obesity, but there are hidden hungers which are the real causes. The obese person has a child savagely hungry for love locked up in his mind. Unless he can learn to let this child out and feed the hunger emotionally rather than physically, he is going to remain obese.

Another hidden hunger is the desire for attention. The person who feels neglected will often turn to food as a substitute. When he says "Pass the potatoes, please," he is really saying "Pay some attention to me!" There is frequently a close connection between love-hunger and the desire-for-attention hunger. Usually, both love and attention are lacking in the individual's life.

One woman whose husband was obese complained constantly to other people about his compulsive eating habits. It didn't require a professional expert to notice that other than to comment on his weight, she never spoke to or about her husband. There were no spontaneous, affectionate words, gestures, or glances between them. As a result of this lack of love and attention, the husband used eating, munching, and nibbling as substitutes for love.

Hunger for security can be a psychosomatic cause of overweight. The adult who felt insecure as a child (perhaps feeding-times during infancy were unsatisfactory and tense either because of parental attitudes or a lack of sufficient milk) continues to feel insecure. Studies have shown that obese adults felt unwanted as children. Eating is a way of building up a physical body which they subconsciously theorize will be difficult to overlook; therefore, their size or bulk, if nothing else, will guarantee them a certain amount of attention from others.

Living in Our Food-Oriented Society

We live in a food-oriented society. Almost every popular magazine contains advertisements for food and drink, and many feature recipes or menus as well as stories about famous restaurants.

Food is traditionally associated with good times and special occasions. And food is often offered as a kind of palliative for discontent, depression, and other "low" feelings. We maintain a persistent belief in the old saying, "Eat, drink, and be merry."

Obese people eat and drink, but they aren't always merry as a result. Yet in a society that places so much emphasis on the enjoyment and importance of food, it is difficult not to give in to the constant temptation to eat.

Paradoxically, we are also living in a diet-conscious society, so that we have an overemphasis on food and at the same time a corresponding emphasis on slimness. We are confused in our goals. As a result, most people eat too much and feel guilty about it.

In the midst of such wide exposure to food and the companionship and sociability associated with food, losing weight requires concentration and willpower.

You and Your Weight Problem

We all have a tendency to notice other people's weight problems and to ignore our own. It is far easier and less traumatic to shake our heads when we see an overweight person than to take a good look at our own scales, or mirrors.

Any weight problem (overweight or underweight) is a very personal problem. You have to face it on the level of your own consciousness. You can lie to yourself; you can evade the facts—but you can't change them.

Let us assume that you have a problem of too much weight. What constitutes obesity? And what can you do about it?

Here are some guidelines for determining where you stand with your weight problem: Ten pounds over the average weight for your age and height should be regarded as a kind of warning; it is giving you notice that unless you stop overeating, you are going to be in serious trouble. Twenty pounds over your normal weight is considered overweight, and ten pounds from there—or thirty pounds over normal —and you have gone into the obese classification.

To handle your weight problem—whether you are still within the danger limits or beyond them—you must be willing to admit that you do have to do something about controlling your weight. Measure your weight against accepted norms, or if you have some doubt about what you should weigh, ask your doctor to give you an examination and help you to determine what your desired weight should be. That weight should then become your goal of achievement.

Obviously, you have to do two things in order to reach that goal: one is to cut down on your eating, and the other is to step up your use of physical energy. Doing these two essential things will give you a slow but steady weight loss.

However, there is a third effort you must make if your weight problem is to be completely and finally solved. You must determine what is causing you to eat too much. That is the *psychic* cause of your weight problem, and until you discover the "why" of your eating habits, you will continue to add excess pounds. Even when you take weight off through a crash or special diet, you will revert to your former weight because any emotional stress will find you back at the table.

Analyze your hidden hungers. See what you can do about satisfying your needs for love, importance, or security, and then do those things. Food is only a stopgap measure. If food were so basically satisfactory, you would not have to keep eating hour after hour, meal after meal.

The combination of less food, more exercise, and an understanding of your own personality will help you keep within the best weight limits.

Overweight and obesity are forms of psychosomatic illnesses which you yourself can control.

Anorexia and Anxiety

Another psychosomatic disorder of the gastrointestinal system is *anorexia,* sometimes called *anorexia nervosa.* It is a loss of appetite or interest in food that results in extreme underweight and emaciation. Anorexia is very often seen in mental patients who may refuse to eat because they believe they will be poisoned. In the emotionally disturbed individual, anorexia is an expression of the self-destructive impulse. People who can't eat have a basic feeling of being unloved and abandoned in life. As a result, they have so little regard for themselves that they do not care about staying alive.

A typical case of anorexia is the individual who lacks self-esteem and is very tense and nervous. Frequently he also suffers from fatigue, partly from lack of food and partly from tension. As a social being this individual is a failure.

He has few if any friends and lacks the ability to make and keep friends.

Anorexia is a form of escape. It is sometimes unconsciously used as a weapon of resentment or hostility. One woman who lost forty pounds and became ill insisted that she could not eat.

"I just can't swallow a thing," she said. "I feel full all of the time."

Although cancer had been suspected, a thorough physical examination showed that she was in good health except for the damage that her inability to eat had caused to her system. Since psychosomatic causes were then suspected, she was sent to me for treatment.

Analysis revealed that when she said she "felt full" she was telling the truth, but the fullness was from emotion. Shortly before my patient lost her appetite, she and her husband had had a violent quarrel over money matters. She recalled that she had said to him, "I'm full up to here with your mismanagement of our finances." At the same time that she had quarreled with her husband, she had had fears of being left alone.

"I know he has his bad faults," she said, "but I just can't face life alone, as my mother had to do when my father walked out on her."

This combination of disgust with her husband and a fear of being abandoned caused her to transfer her "fed-up" feeling with her husband to food. When she couldn't swallow food, it was a symbol of not being able to "swallow" the way her husband handled the family money.

Once she learned the real reason for her anorexia and was persuaded to go with her husband for marriage counseling, she regained her appetite.

Ralph G. was also sent to me because his inability to eat was thought to be psychosomatic in origin. Although he had tried various tonics and pills, Ralph couldn't seem to increase his appetite. Emaciated and haggard, he was forced to stop work because of his lack of energy.

During treatment, Ralph frequently spoke disparagingly

of the company where he had worked for the past twelve years. He finally admitted that he had first noticed the drop in his appetite at about the same time he was passed over for an expected promotion. Ralph felt resentment and a keen sense of disappointment. Not eating was his unconscious response to what he considered to be an injustice.

Like many adults, Ralph's emotional responses to problems and tensions were rooted in childhood experiences. As a child he was a fussy eater. His mother would become very upset when he wouldn't eat, and she finally resorted to bribery. Soon Ralph discovered that he could get attention and gifts, as well as other things he wanted, if he would eat. Food became a weapon in Ralph's emotional approach to problems.

Now that he was angry at the company where he worked, Ralph was using food to express that hostility. What he was saying by not eating was, "I won't eat until I get the promotion I want!" Ralph's mother may have been concerned about his not eating and willing to promise him anything in exchange for a clean plate—but the company was not.

Ralph had to learn to accept reality and to understand that none of us can always have what we want. Not eating as a gesture of resentment and anger was hurting only himself, not the company.

Just as in the problem of obesity, the solution to not being able to eat lies in discovering the hidden causes of your loss of appetite. Understanding your inability to eat is the first step in regaining your appetite.

Stress and Your Stomach

Of all your body organs, your stomach is the one that is perhaps most responsive to your moods and emotional states. Even babies and small children will react to excitement and situations by a change in their digestive processes, sometimes by such a sudden change as vomiting.

The upset stomach is a popular way of explaining what

happens when emotions take over. The word "upset" is a good choice, since in a sense, the person's world is turned upside-down.

A sudden change in circumstances can cause a quick and violent stomach reaction. An individual may feel perfectly well one moment and then suddenly be nauseated if he hears bad news, discovers that he has made a serious mistake, or suffers a loss. Nausea, however, is not only a negative reaction; it may also be caused by good news. As one woman said, "When I got word of my promotion, I was so excited that I actually felt sick. I had to go to the rest room and lie down for a while because I was so nauseated and dizzy."

We are most aware of stomach distress when it is caused by tension or stress. This is natural, because at that particular time most of our attention is focused on ourselves and our immediate situation. Happiness tends to radiate beyond the universe at our own selves, but unhappiness is concentrated within.

The Psychological Significance of Stomach Problems

The person with chronic cramps, nausea, or ulcers can't "stomach" the world. In a very real sense he is chewing on himself rather than others. He is filled with repressed hostility and anxiety. Sometimes these feelings are left over from the past, as in the case of Brenda whose ulcer was caused by her continued resentment of the way she had been treated by her mother during adolescence.

"When I was fourteen, my mother married again, my father having died the previous year. I not only resented the marriage but I was very upset because she and her new husband left at once for a long cruise. I was sent away to school that year. I still remember how unhappy I was. I used to cry a lot and I was sick to my stomach so much that the school doctor insisted that I have tests made. Nothing showed up, but a few years ago I got sick again, and then they discovered I had this bad ulcer."

Brenda's illness recurred as an adult after her mother, now widowed, asked Brenda to come home and live with her. The old resentment flared up, and while Brenda would not tell her mother what her true feelings were, her stomach felt their effect. Result—one very painful ulcer.

George S. had a history of heartburn and a long list of foods which he had to avoid. However, the substances that he blamed for his heartburn—pork, coffee, onions, cucumbers, and other foods—were innocent symbols of the real causes, his wife and his boss. At home, his wife nagged and complained; at work, his boss was demanding and short-tempered. George felt trapped between these two people and their demands and was understandably tense and depressed.

When he changed jobs and his wife accepted some professional marriage counseling, he recovered from his heartburn.

Living With and Coping With Your Nervous Stomach

If you have stomach problems which are psychosomatic in origin, you can not only learn to live with that nervous stomach, but you can learn how to cope with it. Whether your problem is stomach cramps, acid indigestion, nausea, vomiting, or vague feelings of discomfort, you can control your abdominal reactions to stress.

Though reaching for a pill may offer temporary relief, lasting results can be achieved only if you search out the cause of your nervous stomach. Is your indigestion caused by worry? Is it caused by tension? Does any form of excitement produce nausea? Make a point of checking out your emotional state and the situation that immediately preceded your stomach distress. You may find that you were thinking about some unpleasant subject, task, or person. Or you may have been exposed to a tense or hostile situation.

Once you have learned what kind of events precede your attacks, you can make an attempt to rearrange your life so that you can avoid or learn how to cope with the dangerous situations. Perhaps, like George S., you may have to change jobs. Professional counseling may be indicated. Lifetime habits may have to be changed.

Mr. D. had a long history of ulcers and other stomach problems. A quick, aggressive personality, Mr. D. was a businessman who felt compelled to succeed in whatever he did. This compulsion extended to his social and recreational life. Mr. D.'s hobbies were golf and tennis. Unfortunately, he was not well-coordinated enough, and in both games he remained an inept player. It was suggested to him that his gastrointestinal problems might improve if he took up some sport or interest that was less competitive. Mr. D.'s nervous stomach subsided when he learned how to relax. His ulcer had a chance to heal while he developed a new hobby— stamp collecting. When he stopped trying to compete in areas in which he had little likelihood of success, he no longer felt frustrated and nervous.

The Anal Stage of Development

Life patterns are set during the anal stage of development as well as during the oral stage. The anal period usually reaches its height between the ages of two and three, though there may be variations because of individual rates of personality development.

During this stage the attention of the child is centered on the process of defecation, a process that gives him a primary source of erotic pleasure. It also is a determining factor in his relations with his parents, for at this time the parents attempt to impose authority by insisting that the child learn bowel control. The way in which they try to train the child and the way in which the child responds to their requirements has a lasting effect upon his character. And while the parents may seek to impose certain rules, it is the child who decides whether or not he will cooperate. It is also the child who decides whether he is going to get more pleasure from retention, i.e. withholding his feces, or from expulsion. This choice is often reflected in adulthood, when we find the formerly retentive child becoming the constipated adult.

The Adult Anal Character

The adult anal character is easy to recognize. He is frequently subject to severe intestinal trouble, which can range from constipation to diarrhea. He may be unduly preoccupied with his own bowel movements. He may be a chronic taker of laxatives or eater of certain health foods.

There are other personality characteristics which we customarily associate with the adult anal character. The person who as a child got his satisfaction from retention is usually extremely orderly, very frugal, and inclined toward obstinacy. He can be very meticulous about things but at the same time not show the right judgment about priorities. Little things can mean as much to him as big things, and very often he will waste time on the things which are of least importance.

The individual who tried to please his mother by performing as desired and who got his pleasure from expulsion has more confidence as an adult. He is usually generous and outgoing in nature.

It is believed that the collecting and hoarding instincts come from this period of psychosexual development. The miser with his "gold" still has inside him the child who does not want to give up his feces.

Bowel Dysfunction, Anger, and Anxiety

Any kind of bowel dysfunction reflects the early period of childhood training. It is also a reflection of current anger or anxiety. The dysfunction, whether it is constipation or diarrhea, is one way of expressing or discharging anger or anxiety.

People living under stress will respond through their intestines according to the particular emphasis of their bowel training days. That is why one person subject to stress will become constipated while another individual will suffer from diarrhea. If the stress is of a temporary nature, the bowel condition will correct itself when the stress period has ended. Thus, many people report that they suffer from some form of intestinal trouble or irregularity while on a trip. It is popular custom to blame the water or strange food when the cause is actually the person's anxiety. Even the most seasoned traveler has some worries when visiting a strange place.

Loss of a job, family problems, money worries, divorce, fear, death of a loved one are some of the more common causes of bowel dysfunction.

Working with family physicians, I have seen many cases of colitis which were caused by anger, anxiety, or other stresses.

A busy executive who was known for his predatory business habits was almost disabled by colitis. Although he had been on various diets and taken prescribed medication and other remedies, his condition continued to grow worse. Under analysis he revealed that he was very anxious about his success and his image in the eyes of the public. He felt compelled to succeed because his family had been a poor one in a small town where he had felt they were ignored and looked down upon. Driven by an ambition that was actually too much to handle, his body rebelled.

In another case, a young woman was forced to give up her job and most of her social activities because of chronic diarrhea. During treatment she made many references to her unusually close relationship with her parents. She finally admitted that shortly before her intestinal problem began, she had let her parents persuade her to break off her engagement to a young man whom she had met at her office. The anxiety of remaining unmarried plus the desire to please her parents by giving in to them had combined to produce this infantile reaction to her emotional problem. In a sense, she was behaving as an infant again, and because of her health problem, had become financially and psychologically dependent upon her parents.

How can you cope with the problems of intestinal disorders? Just as with the nervous stomach, you have to be willing to take the time to discover the real causes of your physical problem. Look for areas of stress and anxiety in your life, or other personal relationships. The best treatment of your constipation or diarrhea is to treat the causes. You may have to change jobs or reassess your attitudes toward other people.

By remembering that most instances of bowel dysfunction are regressive patterns of behavior, you can help yourself to get over your condition. Only you know the immediate cause of your anger, anxiety, or frustration, and you must learn to relate those causes to your body functions.

Secondary Gain

In any illness there are some advantages and benefits to the individual. If this were not so, there would be fewer cases of psychosomatic illnesses. This is not to say that the individual deliberately chooses to be ill in order to get these advantages. No, most people are not conscious of these benefits, even though they find them enjoyable.

We call these advantages *secondary gains.* A secondary gain is a result of being ill and is different from a primary gain. *Primary gain* is the body-chatter, the expression of unconscious conflict.

Secondary gains can include sympathy, special attention, insurance and disability payments, solicitous concern even from strangers, and the opportunity to be the center of interest.

Herb hated his job in the factory. He thought it was demeaning and beneath his real capabilities. When he was unable to find another job, Herb developed all the gastrointestinal symptoms of severe and disabling stomach trouble. He was convinced that he had cancer. As a result, he was unable to work and had to enter the hospital. He no longer needed to feel guilty about not liking his job; he was now too ill to work. This was the primary gain of his psychosomatic illness. In addition, Herb had become the center of attention of a number of medical specialists. His family and friends were also concerned and kept a constant vigil at his bedside. He found that he could get what he wanted since he had convinced others as well as himself that he was a dying man. All of these advantages were secondary gains.

Most ulcer patients get secondary gains by telling other people of their troubles. They receive sympathy and a certain amount of mothering, which is what many of them basically desire and need. Closely allied to this infantile reaction and need is the diet that ulcer patients have. By having to drink quantities of milk at frequent intervals, they are reliving their infant feeding-days. They are as conscious of their feeding times as any parent is with a baby. They also tend to make others around them conscious of this feeding schedule. I have seen ulcer patients who interrupted a social evening by insisting that they had to have a glass of milk at that precise moment!

The secondary gain serves to take care of the basic unconscious emotional conflict which has caused the illness. It is a compensating factor.

The child who fears a school examination and becomes ill and vomits receives the secondary gains of not having to go to school, having his mother's attention, and possibly of receiving special gifts to encourage him to feel better.

The adult who is dissatisfied with his marriage may develop a gastrointestinal disorder which forces his spouse to pay attention to him. He may require special foods and other considerations. A further secondary gain is that his illness serves as an excuse for not doing what he can to make his marriage a better one. Being sick is considered a valid reason for not assuming normal burdens and obligations.

If you suspect that you have an illness which is psychosomatic in origin, look into this subject of secondary gains. Consider what advantages you are getting from your illness. Are those secondary gains so necessary and useful to you that you can't give up your illness?

Secondary gains can be traps for the psychologically un-wary. And although you may fall into the trap, you don't have to stay in it.

V

That Breathless Moment

A Psychological Look at Your Respiratory System

Your respiratory system consists of a number of important organs—the nose, pharynx, larynx, trachea, bronchi, and lungs—and its function is to bring oxygen into the body and carry away carbon dioxide. Like most other body systems, your respiratory system works automatically, without conscious direction from you. At any time that this system ceases to be an involuntarily-functioning system, you are uncomfortably aware of the change.

"It's as natural as breathing!" is a common saying because we recognize that life and breath are symbiotically related. It is for that precise reason that the respiratory system is affected by your emotions. As with any other part of your body system, viruses can attack the respiratory system. Diseases such as tuberculosis, chronic bronchitis, emphysema, and lung cancer occur. The respiratory system can also be subject to fungus infections and such allergies as bronchial asthma. However, many of the same symptoms that appear in some of the organic diseases and most of the allergies are also triggered by emotional problems. In short, they are psychosomatic symptoms.

Perhaps because breathing is the all-important life sustaining function, it is very quickly and easily affected by emotions. In times of stress, panic, or extreme excitement, the breathing pattern changes. People are usually aware of this change, and in describing it they say such things as "I couldn't get my breath," "It took my breath away," or "I just choked up!" These are all "folk" ways of explaining a psychological effect on the respiratory system.

Other respiratory responses to psychological or emotional factors are coughing, sighing, shortness of breath, rapid and shallow breathing, and chest pains. These are real pain situations, but they do not come from some organic cause, nor can they be cured by pills, shots, or syrups. They can be cured only by discovering the true reason for the respiratory psychosomatic symptoms.

The Psychosomatic Side of the Nose

The nose not only plays an important part in the breathing process, but it has emotional and psychological importance as well. Like the mouth, the nose takes in samples of the outside world. We say we "sniff danger in the air" or that a certain situation "smells."

We also use nasal terms to describe people's actions; for example, we say that they are "nosy" or that they "stick their noses into other people's business."

Just as some individuals express their emotions through their stomachs or bowels, others use their noses. The person who insists he cannot breathe is very much like the person with ulcers; he is calling attention to himself. He is asking for special consideration. Usually, he has great feelings of personal insecurity.

An individual who uses his nasal condition as an emotional outlet will not benefit from operations and other medical treatment of his condition. Medical treatment fails because the condition is psychosomatic and the cause is usually hidden in the patient's unconscious.

Ethel G. had trouble with her breathing and for years had consulted various doctors, insisting that her nasal passages were too narrow. She used nose drops constantly, took allergy pills, and tried other forms of treatment. Finally, she had an operation which she had been assured would correct the problem. While she was in the hospital, Ethel felt better and was enthusiastic about the success of the operation. "For the first time in years I can breathe!" she told her friends. But a few months later Ethel was using nose drops again and complaining that the operation had failed. Her doctor then sent her to me, as it was now obvious that Ethel had an emotional problem.

Even as she sat in my office, Ethel had to interrupt her talking to put drops into her nose. And I had observed that when she looked in her purse and thought she had forgotten her drops, she became momentarily panicky. "I never go anywhere without them," she explained.

"What would happen if you stopped using them?" I asked her.

"I'd stop breathing," was her immediate reply.

"In other words, you think you would die without your nose drops?"

"Well, I guess I really wouldn't, but I wouldn't be comfortable."

The truth was that Ethel subconsciously feared that she really might die, although she knew consciously that this was not true. Analysis gradually brought out details of her childhood which explained her dependence on nose drops and nasal symptoms.

Ethel had been her father's favorite until she was five years old, when a baby boy was born. He immediately became the center of attention. Suffering from jealousy, Ethel went to the baby's crib and pulled the blanket over the baby's head. She was severely scolded by her father, who accused her of trying to keep the baby from breathing by covering up his nose and mouth. This was the first scolding she remembered having received from her father, and it was a traumatic shock to her. Soon after that she had recurring dreams in which she was being covered over with a blanket by her father. That was her childish interpretation of parental rejection. As she grew older, the dreams ceased, but she developed nasal symptoms and a fear of not being able to breathe.

Part of her early shock had been transformed into guilt over what she had tried to do, that is, get rid of the baby. Part had become fear of being punished in a similar way. With treatment, Ethel was able to recognize the connection between that early incident and her later psychosomatic illness. In doing so, she was able to get over her previously unresolved traumatic shock and eventually was able to manage without her nose drops.

The chronic "sniffer" is suffering from some unresolved psychological problem. One patient was using sniffing to cover up his unconscious contempt for other people. Another individual who was extremely depressed complained of

having to sniff in order to breathe. She also said that she
felt like crying much of the time. For her sniffing replaced
crying, since sniffing was an acceptable adult act and crying
was not.

The person with the chronic runny nose is often infantile in nature, exhibiting a reversion pattern of behavior.
This pattern may also include selfishness and emotional immaturity, self-contained behavior which excludes concern for
others.

That Important Sense of Smell

Smell is one of the five senses that give meaning to our
lives. We rarely think about it until it is affected in some
way. Unlike hearing, sight, and the others, our sense of
smell is taken for granted. People vary in their ability to distinguish odors; and air pollution, in addition to the variety
of odors present in modern life, makes it more difficult to be
sensitive to any one particular odor.

Animals, babies, and primitive peoples have a keener
sense of smell than do most adults in modern society. There
are a number of reasons why adults do not have as sharp a
sense of smell. All of their senses are constantly being as-
saulted, and as a result, become less responsive. Modern social custom also builds a stimulus barrier. We train ourselves not to be aware of unpleasant or bad smells. This
attitude is associated at least partially with early bowel
training.

Animals use their sense of smell to track down food
and detect friends and enemies. Their brain structures show
the reason for their sensitivity to odor. In dogs, for example,
about one-third of the temporal lobe is constructed for ol-
factory functions, whereas in modern, adult man about one-
twentieth of the same area is used for those functions.

Primitive societies also use smell as a way of detecting
danger as well as friendly objects.

Infants and dogs can smell hostility and anxiety in others and will respond accordingly. Infants may cry, or dogs may bark or bite.

Odors and smelling become part of personal experience; therefore, what is unpleasant to one individual will not bother another. The psychological dimension to smell comes from memory associations with odors. These memory associations can cause emotional reactions, and in some cases, psychosomatic illnesses.

A woman who became nauseated whenever she smelled chocolate was treated unsuccessfully for this "allergy." Her reaction proved to be of psychosomatic origin and was successfully handled through psychoanalysis. Treatment revealed that as a child of twelve she had been approached by a man who offered her a chocolate bar, which she accepted. Just as she started to eat the candy, the man exposed himself to her. This experience revolted and sickened her, and she always associated it with chocolate candy. After treatment, she was able to put the experience in proper perspective and break the emotional connection between chocolate and the traumatic incident.

Sometimes, emotional problems associated with smells are related to problems of identification. A patient who resented being a woman and suffered from sexual confusion used strong soaps in an effort to cover up what she called "female odor." In a somewhat similar case, a male patient used quantities of sweet-smelling lotion because he wanted to be more feminine. He associated the smell of tobacco and sweat with men and refused to be masculinized in this way. This was all traced back to a negative identification with his father, whom he disliked, and a positive identification with his mother, whom he adored.

Carol was brought to me because she complained that everything smelled bad. She refused to eat and lost several pounds until her weight was far below average for a normal fifteen-year-old girl. In addition, she had become antisocial, spending most of her time alone. Her anxious parents were unsuccessful in communicating with her. At first, Carol would not discuss those matters except to say, in her words,

"Everything stinks!" Later during therapy she explained that she could not eat because all food smelled spoiled, and she did not go anywhere because other places smelled "rotten." One day during a therapy session, Carol suddenly burst out with this statement: "It's me that really smells bad. I'm the one that stinks!" With that opening we were able to discover gradually why Carol insisted that smell was keeping her from living a normal life. She had become friends with a group at school whose attitudes and standards were far different from those she had. Nevertheless, she followed the group's practices, since she admired the leader, a boy who appeared to her to be very knowledgeable about the world. As a result of her association with him and the others in the group, Carol let herself be led into shoplifting, smoking marijuana, and sexual intercourse. In time, the conflict between what she had been brought up to believe was the right conduct and the behavior of the group became too much for her. She not only withdrew from the group, she also withdrew from all other forms of social intercourse. In addition, the conflict between her superego, which said that she had behaved badly, and her id, which said she should enjoy her awakening sexual desires, also proved to be too much for her to handle. She then acquired the fantasy that everything smelled bad, because she could not face the self-accusation that it was she who was bad. Through therapy and analysis, she was able to face her own judgment of her conduct. Convinced that although she had indeed behaved in the wrong way, she also was able to understand that her life was not ruined. She was encouraged to return to normal adolescent life and interests. And since she already had a well-established sense of moral values, she was encouraged to apply them to her life; she had seen what happened when she deviated from those standards.

A male patient, aged thirty-six, had been troubled by an unexplained and persistent itching in his nostrils. Later he complained that he had lost his sense of smell. The itching had started after his wife had been injured in an automobile accident and was unable to have sexual relations with him. He had resorted to masturbation, which brought forth a memory of a childhood experience when he had been told by his father that if he masturbated, his nose would grow, and everyone would know what he had done. The itching he felt was symbolic of this "growing," and the satisfaction he felt in scratching and picking his nose was akin to the satisfaction and relief he felt in masturbating. As a result a strong conflict situation developed which culminated in his claiming that he had lost his sense of smell. This loss was an expression of another fear, which was that he would become impotent if he continued to masturbate. That fear also came from his adolescence and his father's warnings.

If you too have a problem with your nose or sense of smell, it might be wise to see if the origin of that problem is somewhere in your past, particularly in your childhood or adolescence.

Coughing for Attention

A cough is almost sure to get attention. It is in the same category as a nudge, and sometimes not as subtle. A cough can be used to express anxiety, irritation, sulkiness, or nervousness. A cough is a way of saying "Listen to me, pay attention to me!"

If you cough frequently and your family doctor has examined you and found no organic cause, you have a psychosomatic cough. Your next step is to discover why you have a need to cough. That persistent cough is a form of communication, but not a normal form.

Attention-getting is the most frequent reason for psychosomatic coughs. The individual who resorts to this method is often timid and ill at ease with people. He would like to speak up but does not have enough self-confidence to do so, and instead, he coughs. In fact, not infrequently this same individual is unable to speak in public because any effort at talking brings on coughing and choking.

I have observed the coughing-for-attention symptom in

families in which one person was extremely domineering, overshadowing the other family members. In one case, it was the husband who developed a persistent cough after his mother-in-law moved in and assumed control of the household.

At any concert, play, lecture, or other public performance there will be coughing from members of the audience. Some of this coughing is from nervousness or social instability and insecurity, but other coughing is a form of attention-getting. Those coughers are competing with the people on the stage. They are coughing to assert their own importance. As members of the audience they are a public nuisance; as individuals they are in need of counseling.

As an expression of anxiety and nervousness, coughing is a kind of respiratory tic, an unconscious reflex. Many people with nervous coughs, when questioned, will not even remember coughing.

The cough of irritation is meant to be a disruptive element in a social situation. It is usually directed at one person and is a way of expressing hostility. If persistent enough, the cough of irritation can break up a discussion or conversation.

How can you get over your persistent psychosomatic cough? First, you will have to convince yourself that it is not a functional cough and that it serves no necessary purpose in your life. Second, you will have to try to discover why you resort to coughing. Note the times and conditions under which you have this cough. You may find that it is related to stress, to family, to anxiety, or to feelings of insecurity. Having discovered the probable cause, you should take steps to remove it from your life. If, for example, insecurity is the cause, you need to raise your self-esteem.

Many people cough in public because they feel self-conscious. You can get over this by reminding yourself of your true worth as a person. One woman I knew who had that specific problem, discovered that she coughed because she could not engage in small talk and did not know what to do with herself at social gatherings. Instead of continuing to feel socially inferior, she took special pains with her physical appearance and dress when going out. She also made it a point to read a newspaper or newsmagazine so that she not only would have some topics of conversation to contribute but would also be sufficiently informed to be able to respond when others talked to her. As a result, she was no longer troubled by coughing in public. Coughing is just a way of trying to hide feelings of failure.

After you have recognized that your cough is psychosomatic and discovered the reasons for your coughing, you come to the third and sometimes difficult aspect of overcoming it. You will have to break this involuntary habit by conscious and persistent effort. You need to restrain yourself. Each time you start to cough, you will have to try and stop that action. You will have to remind yourself that you do not need to cough. After a short time, you will find that you have broken this habit and you will no longer cough automatically and without reason.

"You Take My Breath Away"

Most breathing problems are related to personality problems or disorders. They are also usually related to interpersonal relationships. The phrase, "You take my breath away," is a very literal one. In some families where a member has breathing difficulties, it has been observed that breathing improved when that member was removed from the family circle. However, since in most cases such removal is impractical, the problem must be dealt with at the rootcause level.

Sixteen-year-old Arlene had extreme shortness of breath which kept her from living a normal, active life. She had shown improvement when sent to another state, but the family could not afford to keep her there. Her medical history revealed that her shortness of breath had started two years before, when she had entered high school. After attending for only one term, she was forced to drop out because of her inability to get around the school building.

When her family doctor could find no physical cause, he suggested that she be sent to a psychiatrist.

Arlene was very cooperative and said she would like to be able to dance and do the other things that her friends were doing. She spoke glowingly of the six months she had spent in another state and how much better she had felt. At the same time, she said she realized that her family could not afford to send her away.

Since it was obvious that there was a connection between starting high school, her family, and her shortness of breath, Arlene was encouraged to talk freely about those subjects. At first she refused to see that there could be a relationship among these factors, but after she became accustomed to the analysis therapy, she admitted that she felt under tremendous pressure when she entered high school. Arlene had had an older sister, Catherine, who had been killed in an accident two years before Arlene began high school. Catherine had been an excellent student and a social leader among her classmates. Arlene was an average student and inclined to be timid. Her family, however, made it plain that Arlene was expected to carry on where Catherine had left off and be the academic and social star her sister had been.

"But I'm not like Catherine!" Arlene exclaimed to me with tears in her eyes.

In trying to force her into a competitive situation, Arlene's family had in a sense taken her breath away. Arlene knew that she could not fulfill their unrealistic expectations and she unconsciously sought for some way out of the situation. A psychosomatic illness was her unconscious solution, since it removed her from the necessity of competing, and her family could not blame her for lack of success when ill health was the cause.

It is always interesting to know why people unconsciously select certain types of psychosomatic illnesses. Sometimes they have a constitutional weakness which they concentrate on; sometimes the illness is suggested by something they have read, or they may take on the illness of a family member or an acquaintance; sometimes the illness itself may be symbolic of its cause. Usually, the patient is unaware of why he has selected his particular form of psychosomatic illness. In the case of Arlene, I discovered that a favorite uncle had emphysema.

Shortness of breath can be caused by chronic anxiety, fear, or worry. If you have a problem with shortness of breath and it has been definitely determined that there is no organic cause, you should examine your life pattern and interpersonal relationships to see where there are stress situations. I have seen and treated cases of shortness of breath where the stress was found in the marriage, in job problems, and in repressed childhood memories.

One man became short of breath soon after his marriage. In his case the cause was not in his marriage but in the fact that he had repressed a primal scene memory which had been a traumatic shock to him. As you recall from Chapter III, we discussed the primal scene in relation to headaches. Seeing his parents in the act of sexual intercourse had frightened him, and his main memory of that act, in addition to the fear, was the sound of their rapid breathing. Now married himself, he reproduced this sound in his breathing pattern and also re-experienced the fear and panic he had felt as a small boy. He claimed that the fear he felt was because he was afraid he would stop breathing, but it was actually the old fear resurfacing.

Don't let repressed memories or other people take your breath away. Find the true cause of your shortness of breath and deal with it. In addition, you can help yourself by taking time each day to stop and make yourself change your breathing rhythm. Deliberately take long, deep breaths. Do not pant. Take exercises which will help you to develop and maintain better breathing habits.

Hyperventilation

One of the most common psychosomatic breathing problems is hyperventilation. Hyperventilation is a kind of emotional over-breathing, during which you may breathe too rapidly and deeply. As a result, you take too much air into the lungs, and the level of carbon dioxide content of the blood is lowered. This combination produces some sudden and dramatic changes in your body. You may experience numbness of the extremities, lightheadedness, a sensation of rapid heartbeat, body cramps, and trembling. Many people faint as a result of hyperventilation.

While hyperventilation has very definite physical features, it is itself caused by emotion. Anxiety and stress, either temporary or chronic, are the most frequent causes. For example, an individual faced with a sudden emergency may hyperventilate and, as a result, faint. Another person who is worried about some personal problem may hyperventilate at regular intervals, giving him a chronic condition of one or more of the symptoms of hyperventilation.

Many people who complain of lightheadedness are hyperventilating because of some emotional problem. One woman had this symptom whenever she was out in a crowd. She was trying to repress feelings of panic and anxiety. Her panic, incidentally, stemmed from a childhood experience during which she had been lost in a crowd at a sports stadium and had almost been trampled by adults rushing for an exit.

You may hyperventilate during your sleep and be awakened by the symptoms—body cramps or numbness and a racing heart. If you are like most people, you will think you are having a heart attack and become panicky. But your panic will only keep you hyperventilating and thus increase your feelings of discomfort. Knowing what has really happened to your body should help you to get over the hyperventilation and relax your body.

Daytime stresses cause nighttime hyperventilation. You do not forget your worries when you sleep; you often act them out in dreams. If the dreams are threatening to you, they will cause you to become physically disturbed. You will not only become a restless sleeper, you may hyperventilate.

Bronchitis, Asthma, and Anxiety

Bronchitis and asthma are symptoms of trying to "cough up" one's feeling of being alone and depressed. They are related to anxiety and stress. In addition, asthma is often the repressed cry for the rejecting mother.

With its choking and wheezing asthma is very similar to the crying of a baby. It is a form of adult crying. Like other psychosomatic illnesses, it is a demand for attention.

If you have bronchitis or asthma, you should take a second look at your childhood, both the remembered parts and those which you may only have heard about. Any areas of neglect during those early years can be the cause of your asthma or bronchitis.

As with most psychosomatic illnesses, the individual is not conscious of the cause, since he would find that cause to be unacceptable to his adult personality. He does not want to admit into his consciousness the fact that he is crying for his mother's attention and love. Although this infantile fixation can take many forms, asthma is one of the most common.

The asthmatic has to face the fact of his unresolved dependency upon his mother, and through analysis and treatment work out the repressed feeling which has resulted in emotional conflict and physical illness.

In some cases the repressed dependence is buried and overlooked until some crisis occurs. A crisis can precipitate feelings of helplessness and abandonment. With these feelings come bronchitis or asthma attacks, and they will persist until the crisis has been resolved or has passed.

In addition to a crisis, any intense emotion or excitement can precipitate asthma attacks. If you have asthma and blame it on the climate or some allergy, you may be suffering needlessly. Using self-analysis, you should examine the mood you were in just prior to your asthma attack. Were there elements of jealousy, rage, anxiety, fear, or sudden sexual excitation?

Change of climate has frequently been suggested to help

asthmatics. Sometimes this has proved beneficial, but in other cases patients become discouraged and depressed when there is no lasting improvement in their health. The asthmatic will not be cured if the same conditions and emotional problems exist in the new location. The man who has asthma attacks because of work-related problems will benefit from a change of location if he is employed in a new, completely different type of work. The man whose asthma attacks are triggered by domestic trouble will not benefit from a geographical change if his marriage continues to be a problem.

Asthma patients usually have a strong desire to be protected and frequently become very dependent upon doctors or upon some form of treatment. They suffer intensely from separation anxiety, and any change in their personal circumstances can cause an asthma attack. Thus, occasionally asthma will not show up until a man or woman decides to marry. The impending marriage will bring out a dependency on the mother and some measure of anxiety and uncertainty about the future.

Tom, an only child, was very much attached to his mother, even though from his childhood on she had sought to make him independent. Despite periods of indifference on her part, Tom continued to seek her approval and concern. At nineteen, Tom married a girl seventeen years old and left home. Almost immediately, he began to have severe asthma attacks. They ceased when he moved back home so that his mother could care for him. When after a time his mother tried to force him to return to his young wife, his attacks returned. This situation continued until his wife took things into her own hands and secured a divorce on the grounds of desertion. Tom had fewer attacks, but they always came either after a quarrel with his mother or when she went away.

Tom refused to admit his dependency upon his mother and instead saw himself in the role of the "good son," despite the fact that his mother resented his attachment. On occasion, she even made fun of him in front of others.

Tom might have continued to suffer asthma attacks,

but his emotional problem was solved when he met an older woman, maternal in attitude, who encouraged his courtship of her. Although his friends remarked about the age difference and the similarities in character between Tom's mother and intended wife, he was happy. Once married, he transferred his dependency from his mother to his wife, and since his wife welcomed this dependency, there were no emotional problems. Tom never suffered from another attack of asthma.

You Can Cope With Your Breathing Problems

You need not be incapacitated by your breathing problems. You can learn to cope with them. Simply remember that they are but symptoms of some emotional distress. You must treat that emotional cause in order to be rid of your symptoms.

Most respiratory ailments are disguised forms of crying. Ask yourself for what reason you are crying. Then ask whether crying will get you what you want. The obvious answer to that last question is No. Childish ways have no place in the adult world. You cannot achieve results by crying. If you have been disappointed in your relationship with your mother and feel unloved, you are depriving yourself of the fullest measure of adult love and life by holding onto this emotional "hang-up." You have a life to live in the present. Why deny yourself the benefits of that life by an inability to breathe without difficulty?

If you felt rejected by your mother, you nonetheless learned to climb out of your crib and walk. You can also learn to use your respiratory system normally. You don't really need to look for love and sympathy by gasping, wheezing, coughing, and sniffing!

VI

"I Haven't the Heart for It"

That Most Known, Least Understood Body Organ

No other body organ is so much or so often thought about as the heart, and no other body organ has so much folklore and superstition associated with it. The heart has been given an identity of its own by poets, early philosophers, and a generally romantic but misinformed public.

In early times the heart was thought to be the repository of all feelings and emotions. It was Aristotle who claimed that the heart was where the soul was located. Many comments in the Bible attribute feelings to the heart: "A man's heart deviseth his way," "He that is of a merry heart hath a continual feast," "As he thinketh in his heart so is he." Both in religion and poetry the heart is described as *contrite, clean, aching, evil, loving, full,* or *broken.* Individuals are described as being *stout-hearted,* or in some cases, *black-hearted.*

There is a relationship between those early beliefs and psychosomatic illnesses affecting blood pressure and the heart. We know that the heart is a pump-like muscle, by which our blood performs its necessary circulatory functions; yet there remain vestiges of those old primitive feelings about it. Most people retain an awe and a superstitious regard for the heart because they know their lives depend on its proper functioning.

It is precisely for that reason that so many of the problems associated with the heart are psychosomatic in origin. The heart is a muscle, but it is also another of our emotional barometers. Some people simply respond through and with the heart and the blood pressure rather than through some other part of the body. As we will see later in this chapter, there are psychological reasons why heart trouble becomes the psychosomatic choice of so many individuals.

One of the proofs of our mystical regard for the heart is shown in the controversy over heart transplants. Not only is there medical controversy regarding the reliability of such operations, but questions of the morality of heart transplant operations have also been raised. No matter how technological and scientific our society becomes, we can never quite get away from this emotional feeling about the heart, for our literature and customs are permeated with its very special mystique.

Heart Action and Anxiety

When there is a disturbance of the heart action which is psychosomatic in origin, there is also a hidden history of anxiety or dread. Sometimes that history is so well hidden that the patient himself is unaware of what is causing him to suffer from heartbeat irregularities.

In psychosomatic heart problems of this type, the person is aware of the changes in his heartbeat and suffers from an added anxiety because of this fact. Usually, he feels that he is going to die because of the sudden and pronounced changes in his heartbeat. The panic which he then experiences adds to his physical distress.

The most common forms of heartbeat disturbance are tachycardia (very rapid heartbeat), fibrillation (extra beats), palpitations, or any arrhythmia, which is a change in the normal heart rhythm. Patients, in describing their feelings during these times, have used such phrases as "I thought my heart would jump right out of my chest," "My heart would skip and jerk a lot," "My heart seemed to stop for a second," and "My heart was racing."

Everyone I have questioned about such incidents reported that their symptoms worsened as they concentrated on them. They also reported feeling faint, nauseated, and hot, with sudden perspiration, particularly of the face and hands. After the "attacks" had subsided, they felt tired and weak.

If these descriptions fit your symptoms, you may, like many others, be contributing to your problem by repressing feelings of anxiety and dread. You can overcome this heart condition by making some changes in your life or in your outlook on life. To do this successfully, you will have to learn to develop a candid analysis of your actions and emotions that preceded your attacks of heartbeat irregularity.

That is what Earl H. did to help himself get over tachycardia. For a number of years Earl had frequent periods of rapid heartbeats, and he lived with the fear that he would die from a heart attack. During some of his attacks, he felt, in his words, "completely washed out." He had gone to his doctor, but when told he had no organic heart disease Earl became angry and consulted another doctor—with the same results. Five doctors later, he was willing to concede that perhaps his own diagnosis was incorrect and that he needed psychiatric help and counseling.

In my office, he presented a classic picture of anxiety. His face was flushed, his hands moist, and he had a facial tic and a nervous cough. He said that his attacks of rapid heartbeats had increased in the past year and that he had developed a great fear of death.

I asked him to think back to the events immediately preceding these attacks. He recalled that on one occasion he had been upset because his daughter had been late in coming home from a dance. On another occasion he had been involved in a minor traffic accident. More recently, an attack had been preceded by watching a television program which dealt with drugs and young people. "I got to thinking about my daughter," Earl explained. "All of a sudden I could see her mixed up in something like this, and I began to worry about what she was doing when she went out."

Earl was not only a chronic worrier, but he had a whole host of unresolved anxieties, many of which he had unsuccessfully attempted to repress. Many of his worries and anxieties were without any real foundation, but he let his imagination take over.

When he was able to see the connection between his anxieties and his tachycardia, Earl was willing to concede that he did not have an organic heart condition after all. He then went to the next step, which was to try and apply some logic to his anxieties.

Anxiety is like a fire; if uncontrolled it will burn and destroy. But anxiety can be fought and controlled by logical thinking. When applied by Earl, logical thinking, resulted in a diminishing anxiety level and an end to his heart problem. He learned to stop and analyze an anxiety when it came to him. He did not continue to let his imagination run wild. He found, in time, that he really had fewer worries than he had thought, and that most of the unpleasant things he had anticipated never actually happened.

You can use the same system in your own life. Note what your feelings were at the time of your attack and what happened before it occurred. In some cases there is a time lag, perhaps of several hours, between the emotional cause and its effect. One man who had work-connected anxieties seemed perfectly in control of himself, but would wake up during the night with severe heart palpitations. At first he blamed it on his eating habits and went on a strict diet, but the palpitations continued. Finally, he was able to find the connection between his work and his nighttime attacks.

By analyzing your activities and emotions, you will be able to discover a pattern that will show you what is causing your problems with your heart. You may have to treat the cause in some drastic fashion, as by changing jobs, but usually it is sufficient to change your attitude toward the things that have been bothering you.

Discover the cause of your anxiety, and treat your anxiety by facing up to or removing its source. Knowing why you become anxious is only the first step in solving your anxiety-related heart problem. Above all, you have to convince yourself that you are not in danger of dying from your psychosomatic heart illness.

Destruction Anxiety

One anxiety often repressed by sufferers of arrhythmia is the destruction anxiety, which may be defined as an impulse to kill. This impulse gives rise to a conflict between the id, which says "Kill," and the superego, which says "No!" Ordinarily, the impulse is controlled in that it never finds expression in any actual form. However, the conflict between the id and the superego frequently results in some form of psychosomatic illness that is centered around the heart. Feeling almost overwhelmed by his emotional feelings, the individual attempts to transfer his destructive impulses to himself. By doing this, he redirects the impulse and at the same time punishes himself for his aggressive thoughts.

A very common form of destruction anxiety is seen in cases where there is competition or some form of rivalry between father and son. As a child the son may have experienced the common fantasy of wishing for his father's death, a fantasy resulting from resentment of the father's power and superiority. As an adult, the son may compete in his career in such a way that he tries to be more successful than his father. At the point, however, that he succeeds and is beginning to surpass his father, he may develop cardiac symptoms. In a sense, the son is horrified at his unconscious death wish for the father, so he pulls back from the brink by simulating (also unconsciously) some form of heart trouble.

Cardiac Neurosis

Cardiac neurosis, also known as cardiophobia, is a state of anxiety in which an individual insists that he has heart trouble and exhibits the symptoms associated with a heart condition. Is he malingering? No, he actually has those physical symptoms and he is suffering. The shortness of breath, palpitations, and rapid or irregular heartbeat are real. But there is no physical cause for these symptoms despite the patient's claims. Doctors see many such cases of cardiac neurosis.

There are a number of reasons why cardiac neurosis appears so frequently. We have already spoken of the vast amount of folklore surrounding the whole concept of the heart. In addition, there are well-publicized facts about the heart and heart disease. This combination has focused attention on the heart. Not everyone is cognizant of what happens when he suffers some disability or malfunction of other body organs, but everyone knows what happens when his heart stops or is affected in any way. An individual tends to assume that despite a damaged lung or kidney, he will somehow live, but a damaged heart means only one thing— the possibility of sudden death!

There is no doubt that an informed public means that many people survive genuine heart attacks, because knowing the symptoms, they seek medical attention in time, yet there are many other cases in which individuals adopt cardiac symptoms simply because they know what they are. Every pain in the chest is not a heart pain! Many chest pains are caused by tension, indigestion, excitement, or gas. Recently, some medical associations have made it a point to list genuine heart attack symptoms as compared with the symptoms of false heart attacks.

Sometimes, simulated heart trouble is a case of misplaced identification. The individual who reports this heart condition has often been exposed to heart trouble through the illness of a family member or close friend. If an important public figure is reported to have a heart condition, people prone to psychosomatic illnesses will think that they, too, have the same symptoms.

Occasionally, by his questions or physical examination, a doctor may unwittingly suggest cardiac problems to a patient. In these cases, however, it should be understood that the patient is unconsciously *looking for* a disease. He is eager to seize upon any possible action or word by the doctor which he can interpret as his individual ailment. Thus, a slight hesitation by the doctor or a change in his voice tones assumes an unnatural importance. A patient who has a functional heart murmur which does not affect him in any way may become a cardiac invalid simply because he refuses to accept the truth about his condition. Fear plays a tremendous role in cardiac neurosis.

Madeline, twenty-six years old, gave up her job and stayed at home after having a physical examination. She told her worried family and friends that she had a heart condition and was no longer able to work or live a normal life. "I'm just waiting for the end," she said. When they checked with the doctor, however, he expressed surprise. Her physical examination had shown no signs of heart trouble. Madeline rejected this news, and instead developed such symptoms as shortness of breath and chest and arm pains. She refused to leave her room, saying that any excitement or exercise would be fatal.

Talking with Madeline brought out the fact that her heart trouble had its background in her past; it was, more specifically, what we call an iatrogenic illness. An iatrogenic illness is one that is unintentionally induced or in some way aggravated by the examining doctor. Madeline was basing her self-diagnosis on these facts: the doctor had listened to her heart and then suggested an electrocardiogram; he had asked for her family history and nodded when she said her grandmother had died of heart failure. Madeline refused to accept as fact that the doctor required all of his patients to have electrocardiograms, and that nodding was just a habit of his. The truth was that Madeline had gone to the doctor unconsciously looking for some disease or disorder.

Madeline was not a happy person. She felt that she had failed in life because she had not gone to college. She resented living at home, and yet she lacked the will to move away. She saw, in her words, "No way out of my dreary life." Madeline confessed that many times she had wished she were dead, but added quickly that she knew it was a "wicked" wish. Having heart trouble was Madeline's way out.

Undoubtedly, she had selected heart trouble because of her grandmother, with whom she had spent her summer vacations as a child. "I missed her very much when she died," Madeline said. "I always felt closer to her than to anyone else in the family." It was this feeling of closeness that made Madeline assume the same form of illness.

If you suspect that you are suffering from cardiac neurosis, you should check to see if there is some family or emotional connection with heart trouble. Also try to determine what factors could have suggested heart trouble to you. It could be something you read or heard. It could be a misinterpretation of what a doctor has said to you. You also must answer the questions of whether or not you are looking for a way out of problems or troubles, and if a heart attack seems like a suitable substitute for suicide.

Don't be afraid to seek professional help if you have symptoms of heart trouble; but if your doctor tells you that you do not have any functional disorder, and you cannot believe that, look for the psychological causes. You may have to consult with a trained psychiatric counselor or psychiatrist to discover why you have chosen heart trouble as your particular illness.

Essential Hypertension

Hypertension is high blood pressure. Blood pressure is the pressure exerted by the blood upon the walls of the arteries. Various factors influence this blood pressure, and these include the force of the heartbeat, the amount of blood and its thickness, and the elastic quality of the artery walls.

As with other conditions, many cases of hypertension are caused by emotional problems, tension, and anxiety. High blood pressure is actually a physical substitute for blowing one's top. We recognize this relationship when we say such things as "I was so mad, it really made my blood boil!"

High blood pressure is another manifestation of the self-destructive impulse. It is aggression unconsciously directed against the self. The individual may be vaguely aware that he doesn't feel just right. He may be very much aware of his tension and anxiety, but he doesn't realize what he is trying to do to himself.

One man who had essential hypertension had developed this condition after a boating accident. He blamed it on nervousness resulting from the accident, but psychoanalysis revealed that he was suffering from extreme feelings of guilt over the accident. As a result of his poor judgment, the boat was wrecked and one passenger, a young boy, drowned. My patient felt that he should be punished and pay in kind— that is, with his own life. Like many people, he had a strong moral feeling against suicide, but he still felt that he should be dead. His blood pressure rose in response to the tension he felt as a result of this conflict between his feeling that he should be punished and die, and a natural desire to live. There was a strong possibility, however, that his high blood pressure would kill him unless a way were found to relieve his tension and guilt. Fortunately, he was able to work out his feelings and get rid of them through treatment. When he did this, his blood pressure dropped to its normal level.

It is important to understand that high blood pressure is dangerous. Hypertension may be caused by emotions, but the physical ailment is very real. Continued high blood pressure can cause crucial blood vessels in the heart and brain to burst. A patient then may suffer from angina, coronary disease, fainting, or strokes. Serious physical and mental disability can occur. Death can occur. People with high blood pressure have a choice to make: they choose life or death, depending upon whether they decide to take the steps necessary to lower their blood pressure or to continue in the ways that keep their blood pressure up at the danger level.

If you have high blood pressure, you need to find out the causes and then act on them. You would not knowingly take poison; yet you may be acting in some way or responding to situations in a way that effects your body in the same manner as poison.

One of the most frequent causes of hypertension is rage, particularly accumulated rage. If you have ever seen anyone in a rage, you have observed his red face, distorted blood vessels, and choking speech. At that time the individual's blood pressure rises to an explosive high. Imagine this scene repeated at regular intervals, and you can see how rage can damage the heart and blood vessels. Accumulated rage has the same effect, for the person who carries within himself a constant feeling of anger is putting tremendous pressure on his body's system. His blood pressure rises in proportion to the anger he builds up.

Another way of visualizing the dangers of hypertension is to picture what happens to a tire if you continue to apply air pressure to it. The tire walls will stretch just so far; then there will be a blowout. This can happen to your blood vessels.

Obesity is another cause of hypertension. The overweight person puts a strain on his body, and particularly on his heart and blood pressure. Going back to our analogy of the tires, the obese person is like the driver who so overloads his truck that the tires simply collapse under the weight.

There are two ways of controlling your blood-vessel spasms and tensions. One is to find suitable ways of discharging your aggressive impulses. The man or woman who takes pride in "keeping things in" or under control is the very person who is apt to suffer from a coronary or stroke. Obviously, aggression cannot be released in an antisocial way, but it can be discharged by participation in some physical activity. A sports game is one solution, a brisk hike or some housework or yard work are others. One woman scrubs her kitchen floor when she finds tension building up; by the time she has finished her task, she has gotten rid of her aggressive feeling. Another woman rakes the yard or performs some other outdoor job.

A second way of controlling the build-up of tension that results in high blood pressure is to schedule periods of relaxation in your life. In the next chapter I shall further discuss this relationship between relaxation and psychosomatics, for our attitude toward leisure has a very definite bearing upon our health problems. It is a chilling but true observation that "all work and no play makes Jack a dead boy!"

Nighttime and Your Heart

If you have a psychosomatic heart condition, you will find that nighttime will pose a special problem for you.

Your heart condition will bother you more at that time. You may feel perfectly well and physically at ease during the day but become ill during the night. Some patients have reported that they dreaded going to bed at night because they feared having a heart attack, heart illness, or discomfort.

There are reasons why you are more aware of your heart and suffer from feeling ill during the night hours. Night is a lonely time. You are no longer surrounded by people and things. It is a quiet time when noise is at a minimum. In the darkness you are aware of every sound, including the sound of your own heart.

As one patient said, "All of a sudden I feel terribly alone and very, very vulnerable. I hear my heart pounding, and I am aware that only my heart stands between me and death. In a few minutes I think it is beating in a strange pattern, irregularly, jerkily. I think it may only be minutes before it will stop. I panic then and think I can't breathe. I only get relief by sitting up in bed." This speaker, a man in his fifties, led an active life as a stockbroker. He was in good physical health, but he admitted that he worried a lot about his work and his own finances. When he went to bed, all of his thinking would suddenly focus on himself and his work. He would replay the day's activities, anticipate nervously what might happen the next day, figure out how much money he owed, and so on.

Through treatment he learned to put aside his work when he went home. He also made himself realize that he had no real financial problems, and finally he stopped being as concerned about his personal finances. As a very practical measure, he bought a radio which had an automatic timer that turned the radio off after an hour. Each night, he went to sleep listening to music, no longer tempted by silence into listening to the sound of his heartbeats.

You may get some relief by doing something like that to help yourself get over those first few minutes of the night. It is also wise to try to become as relaxed as possible by reading something pleasant or watching a television comedy before trying to fall asleep. Whatever you do or choose to look at, the idea to keep in the front of your mind is that your purpose is to relax. Being relaxed means that you can go to sleep more quickly and easily, thus eliminating the time when you may worry yourself into being ill.

These same suggestions can help you if you are the type of person who goes to bed, falls asleep, and then wakes up in a panic, with heart pounding or beating irregularly and having chest pains and difficulty breathing. "I always think, 'This is it'," a patient said. "I wonder if I should get my husband up and have him call the doctor. In my mind I can hear the ambulance coming, see the flashing lights; but at the same time, I know that it's too late!"

Yes, tensions can erupt in restless sleep and dreams which, in turn, can cause you to waken suddenly and have these symptoms. However, if you are able to go to sleep with your tension level lowered and your worries resolved, there will be less likelihood of your being awakened in a panic.

One of the things you should do is assure yourself that you are not having a fatal heart attack. Calm yourself. Try to think of something pleasant, perhaps some place you have visited or something enjoyable you have done. One man used to imagine that he was fishing on a lake where he had gone as a boy.

Broken Hearts and Broken Lives

The "broken" heart is a favorite literary device and artistic symbol. The popularity of the concept of the heart as a "shatterable" object perhaps reaches its zenith during the valentine season. Although we know that in actuality a heart cannot be broken, it remains a believed fiction; thus, we still hear people say, "I was broken-hearted," or "She broke her mother's heart."

Just what is a "broken heart"? It is merely a cliché to describe a feeling of overwhelming sadness. The person who says his heart is broken means that he is almost overcome by his burden of discouragement and depression. He knows that his actual heart—the pump, the muscle—is not damaged in any way. The heart of which he speaks is a fictional one, yet the feelings he has can be very real and very devastating.

A broken heart can mean a broken life. The individual who is depressed and unhappy no longer functions efficiently. He loses contact with reality and in some cases, withdraws from social and other activities. However, people respond in individual ways to broken hearts, and some attempt to compensate by being overactive. They become overachievers and may work themselves into actual heart disease.

What causes a broken heart? It can be a severe disappointment, a sudden shock, or some action that results in loss of self-esteem and confidence. Most broken hearts come from some difficult interpersonal relationships—disappointments in love or marriage, and unsatisfactory parent-child relations. Broken hearts are also caused by inability to become reconciled to changes in life plans.

The reasons causing people to feel that they have broken hearts are as varied as the individuals themselves. The blow that would finish off one person will scarcely be noticed by another. Like the proverbial straw that breaks the camel's back, the immediate cause of heartbreak can be mysteriously minor—except to the person involved. While small in itself, however, it is the culmination of a series of trauma-causing incidents or situations. It is the "final blow," something that has happened one time too often!

In one of Emily Dickinson's famous short poems she writes of a broken heart in these words:

> *Not with a Club, the Heart is broken*
> *Nor with a stone—*
> *A whip so small you could not see it*
> *I've known*
> *To lash the Magic Creature*
> *Till it fell.*

Can a broken heart be a cause of death? Early physicians thought so, and it was commonly listed as a cause, particularly during the seventeenth and eighteenth centuries. We no longer will accept such a diagnosis as a bona fide cause of death; yet a broken heart may be the real culprit, although some disease or accident is listed on the death certificate.

We have already mentioned those who are driven to overachieve, and as a result weaken their bodies and shorten their lives. There are also people who because of their unhappiness no longer take care of themselves properly. They fail to eat when they should, do not get enough rest, and in general lose the will to live. They may die of pneumonia, malnutrition, or from a mishap caused by a failure to use good judgment; but the real cause of death is a broken heart, or perhaps more precisely, not wanting to live anymore.

In folklore and fiction, it has always been supposed that broken hearts are suffered mostly by women. Men are depicted as strong creatures who are not susceptible to disappointments and other disasters. The truth is that broken hearts, like any other form of psychosomatic illness, are not confined to either sex. Broken hearts happen to individuals. They are another form of psychosomatic response to the traumatic experiences of life.

Don't Be Afraid of Your Heart

Fear for your heart can give you a psychosomatic heart condition. Understand in scientific terms what your heart is and what it does. Don't continue to think of your heart in emotional terms, because to do so makes it a Yo-Yo for your feelings. With an emotional view, your feelings are continually fluctuating: One minute you are happy; the next minute you are depressed. Your heart reflects these changes, and you can easily develop the habit of using it to express your emotions. As with any psychosomatic illness, you can either talk yourself into a psychosomatic heart condition or out of one.

If you have some questions about the functioning of your heart, go to your doctor and get his opinion. Don't try to diagnose your own condition, for that will only compound your fears. Keep a diary of your emotions and discover what occurrences and moods give you that chest pain, those palpitations, or other heart disturbances.

Just as you can change your life habits so that you can live comfortably and long with a damaged heart, so can you learn to live *without* a psychosomatic heart illness.

If You Can't Play,
You Won't Work

Leisure and Your Health

Your state of health is directly connected to your concept and use of leisure time. Many psychosomatic illnesses are caused either by lack of leisure time or poor use of it.

An individual's inability to make proper use of his leisure time is also an indication of a psychosomatic problem. This problem is frequently one of extreme restlessness, which I shall discuss later in this chapter.

Why is properly-utilized leisure so important? Why is it so essential for good mental and physical health? In rather simplified terms, the answer is that man is not a machine. His endurance has limits, but those limits can be stretched by combining work with leisure. Leisure is an essential ingredient in the life of the well-integrated, successful person.

Miguel de Cervantes, in his classic *Don Quixote de la Mancha* wrote: "The bow cannot always stand bent, nor can human frailty subsist without some lawful recreation." And George Bernard Shaw said: "A day's work is a day's work, neither more nor less, and the man who does it needs a day's sustenance, a night's repose, and due leisure whether he be painter or ploughman."

What Cervantes, Shaw, and a host of other writers, including this one, are saying is that leisure is an integral part of life. There must be a work-leisure cycle in an individual's life. Moreover, this cycle should be a balanced one, for too much work or too much leisure will result in psychosomatic symptoms. Just as an individual's needs for sleep and food vary from those of his neighbor or even from other members of his family, so do his leisure needs vary.

It is up to you to discover the right proportions of work and leisure in your life. Once you have established a rhythmic work-leisure cycle, you will find that better health will automatically be one of the benefits.

Leisure should mean recreation, relaxation, and rest. If it doesn't, then you are making work out of your leisure, (That too is something I will discuss at greater length later in this chapter). Recreation literally means "re-create," and when you are using your leisure time best, you are "re-creating" your personality. The process is analagous to re-charging a battery system. We all know what happens to a flashlight or a radio when the batteries run down. First of all, there is no power, second, there is no practical function from the object—the flashlight doesn't give enough light, and the radio cannot be heard. The same thing happens to you when you are without proper recreation: you run down and cease to function efficiently and effectively. One of the reasons is that lack of sufficient recreation can result in fatigue, sleeplessness, colds, gastrointestinal disturbances, and other forms of psychosomatic illness.

Even though they know that leisure is necessary for good health, some people neglect this area of their lives. Perhaps they think they don't have time—but do they have time for sickness? Emotional attitudes formed in childhood may be responsible for neglect of leisure; or perhaps these people simply do not know how to handle their free time. Perhaps they have become too stiff and restrictive in their lives because they don't understand the psychology of regression.

If a lack of constructive use of leisure is a contributing factor in your psychosomatic illness, the first step you must take is to try to determine the background of your attitude toward leisure.

No Time for Fun

"Leisure!" snorted Edward S. "I have no time for fun!"

"But you have time to complain about not feeling well," was my reply.

"That's different, and anyway, fun has nothing to do with my ulcers."

I was able to show Edward that he was wrong and that in his case there was a direct connection between his not having time for fun and his ulcers.

Edward S. was not only a perfectionist but a hard

worker. He had started out with a small retail hardware store and had built it up into a large chain of stores. When he had first gone into business, he took care of everything from ordering to selling; now there were too many details for him to keep track of, yet he continued to try to oversee the entire business. As a result, Edward had no time for anything except business. He was forced by his attitude to live at a frantic pace which left him no opportunity for relaxation. In addition, his physical health was steadily deteriorating. When he did stop to draw a breath, it was only to complain about his poor health. His ulcers were caused by his unwillingness to slow down and take time for recreation. The constant pressure in his life, which was of his own choosing, was eroding not only his stomach lining but his peace of mind too.

It took considerable persuasion to make Edward rearrange his schedule to allow time for leisure, but once he had done so, he began to feel better. In addition, he reaped a dividend he had not anticipated—he was able to do his work more efficiently because he was more refreshed and not so tired. Time for leisure, as he learned, was not wasted time. It was an aid to good health and good judgment.

The Calvinist Doctrine of "Work Is Good and Play Is Bad"

Only in the United States do we have the paradox of the Calvinist doctrine that work is good and play is bad and, at the same time, a society which is self-indulgent and very much concerned with pleasure. This national contradiction is experienced on the individual level so that guilt often accompanies leisure.

In the eighteenth and nineteenth centuries, there was more justification for a doctrine of strict application to duty. Life was harsh and work was essential for survival. Work meant long hours of labor (usually twelve), and the work week was six days long. Further, since puritanical religious views predominated, the seventh day was deemed by many people not suitable for recreation. Sundays were not days of leisure as we know them, but simply days on which no work was done. Recreation was for the rich, and even they were admonished to use their time in good works rather than in idleness.

Of course, unrelenting work was necessary to the rapid development of a new nation. Now, however, conditions have changed, but vestiges of the Calvinist doctrine remain to plague the leisure of millions.

Many people feel compelled to keep busy because they cannot escape their feelings of guilt. These feelings can be traced back to childhood conditioning. The child who is brought up in a family that puts particular emphasis on work will find it almost impossible to relax when he is an adult.

As one woman told me, "I would love to read more books, but as a child I was never allowed to read until all of my assigned tasks were done. Even today, I always feel that I must have all of my work done before I sit down and read. When I do stop and read, I feel guilty about it, and after a short time I get up and do some kind of work. The other evening, for example, I sat down to read, but then I remembered that I had some ironing to do, so I put my book away and ironed. I went to bed feeling very unhappy and frustrated and angry with myself. My husband says I'm foolish, but I can't seem to get away from my childhood training!"

Her husband was right. She was foolish, but she was also correct in stating that it was difficult to get away from the past. She had to accept the fact that her childhood was over, and that now she had the right to control her own life. She had to learn that times had changed and her personal circumstances were not as they had been in her childhood. By planning, she could do her work and still have time to read without suffering from feelings of guilt. She also had to learn that some tasks could safely be postponed while she read or enjoyed some form of recreation. She did not have to feel that all her work had to be done before she could relax. It is doubtful, as I explained to her, that anyone can ever say that his or her work is "done." Periods of relaxation and recreation are necessary between work segments. Seeing life as a combination of work and recreation rather than composed of two opposing forces helped her to get over her guilt feelings.

The child who is raised in a home atmosphere in which there are sensible attitudes toward chores and fun will grow up to be a mature, well-adjusted adult. He or she will be able to handle work situations and recreation without putting undue emphasis on either one.

Your emotional attitude toward leisure is part of your intellectual inheritance in the sense that your parents have given it to you. That attitude can be changed, however, to be more in keeping with your own life style. It can be changed to insure that you have the maximum amount of enjoyment and good health in your life.

The Role of the Father in Determining Attitudes Toward Leisure

In counseling patients who had problems related to their inability to relax and use their leisure time, I discovered that when their difficulties stemmed from childhood, it was almost always the father who was responsible for their attitudes.

The father has played a traditional role in making children believe that idleness is evil. Many patients recalled being admonished for idleness and having their father's words reinforced by such quotations as the famous one from Isaac Watts: "For Satan finds some mischief still/For idle hands to do." One woman remembered having to cross-stitch that motto on a sampler when she would have preferred to be out playing.

Sometimes this early training can have tragic results, as in the case of Mrs. L., a woman who was known throughout the city for her many activities. She was a familiar figure in civic organizations as well as in her church activities. She was also a social leader whose home was the scene of many luncheons and other gatherings. Then one day Mrs. L. collapsed. Her family and friends were not only shocked but bewildered, for Mrs. L. had seemed indestructible.

Mrs. L.'s daughter was near collapse herself as she explained what had happened. "My mother was always so energetic," she said. "She never sat down but was always busy for as long as I can remember. Now she doesn't have any interest in anything. She just lies in bed. She says she is too weak to get up."

She went on to say that the family doctor had said that there was really nothing wrong with Mrs. L. in a physical sense, other than the tiredness which she would normally have recovered from after a few days' rest. However, three weeks had passed, and Mrs. L. was no stronger.

Psychiatric treatment revealed that Mrs. L. had been raised in a strict home where any form of idleness was punished by her father. Unfortunately, Mrs. L. could not rid herself of the attitude that being idle was also being wicked. She realized how wrong her father had been, but even though she was now married and had a home of her own, she could not change. She wanted to be able to relax, but she felt driven to keep busy. The conflict between her father's ways and her own wishes became so strong that finally she unconsciously took the only way that seemed acceptable to escape her dilemma—she returned to a state of childlike dependency. In this state she had no responsibility and felt that she could not be blamed for doing nothing.

After treatment, Mrs. L. was able to resume a normal life, with less activity and more relaxation in it. She had gotten over her unconscious belief that repudiating her father's ideas about idleness meant a repudiation of him as a person. She learned to lead her own life and still retain her filial feelings toward her father.

It was Mrs. L.'s superego that was causing her trouble. As we said in Chapter III, the superego is one of the three psychological divisions of the brain. It is the repository of the guilt system—the moral code or conscience. It is the superego that says No to you when you are tempted to do something contrary to your ethical principles. Those ethical principles are given to you by your parents, teachers, and other authority figures. The superego is a storehouse of your concepts of right and wrong; it works like an ever-present recording to remind you of what you are supposed to be thinking or doing. When there is conflict between the ego—the conscious part of your mind—and the superego, there is also a reaction from your body or mind, or both.

When Mrs. L. experienced this inter-psychic conflict, she reacted by becoming physically weak and mentally disinterested. Another person might have turned to alcohol or drugs. Many people develop psychosomatic illnesses. They use those illnesses as means of escaping the tension generated within themselves by the ego-superego conflict.

If an inter-psychic conflict is keeping you from enjoying your leisure, you will have to settle that conflict. Understanding that times have changed may help you put the standards of your parents in proper perspective. You don't have to work as hard as they did; you have more leisure hours under present work-social conditions. You may have to keep reminding yourself that you are living in today's world and not in yesterday's.

To Watch, To Eat, To Sleep—Or, Why Leisure Time Can Be So Boring!

Never before in history have millions of people been so captured by a mechanical device as they are by television. From both social and psychological viewpoints, television has positive and negative features. It has an infinite capacity for enriching the lives of viewers, but it also has the potential for stupefying them.

As a psychiatrist, I am most concerned with the psychological influences of television. Unfortunately, watching television has become the primary recreation of too many individuals. If you follow what has become a standard pattern of leisure time—spending hour after hour in front of the television set—you are cheating yourself of the best use of your free time. There is a kind of routine in which the viewer watches, has one or more drinks, eats a snack (or eats continually), and dozes. At the end of the evening, the viewer gets up, brushes crumbs onto the floor, deposits the empty cans and dirty dishes in the kitchen, and goes groggily off to bed. Is this the way you spend your time?

Why am I, a psychiatrist, concerned about this kind of behavior, and what has television viewing to do with psychosomatic illness? The fact is that excessive television watching can be a contributing factor in psychosomatic illnesses. The individual who spends hour upon hour in front of his set is not maintaining his development as a personality; he is simply vegetating. Television contributes to his lack of exercise and to poor eating habits, but more than that, it makes the individual into a dull person. And dullness keeps him from being a mentally healthy, well-adjusted person.

"I'd like to get out and do more," Ted said, "but I'm too tired. When I get home from work, I just want to sit down and relax, so I watch TV."

"Are you any less tired after you have 'relaxed' all evening?" I asked him.

"No," he admitted. "I can't understand it. I don't do anything, but I still feel just as tired, and besides, I have a lot of aches and pains most of the time. Anyway, television helps because it kills time. I don't know what I'd do with my evenings if I couldn't watch TV."

It would be very difficult to convince Ted and thousands like him that his tiredness and aches and pains are caused by his lack of activity and few interests. In Ted's universe there is only himself at one end and television at the other. It is to him a satisfying and all-absorbing universe. Even his wife is only on the periphery of this universe, and their sole sharing is in the programs they both watch. Television is not only killing time for Ted, it is also killing *him,* just as it has destroyed his social and family life.

There is another aspect of television that has direct bearing on the high incidence of psychosomatic illnesses among steady viewers. The commercials and their preoccupation with health problems and body functions focus the attention of viewers on these subjects. There is a constant suggestion that a person should expect to suffer from various ailments, ranging from "irregularity" to "sleeplessness." Body malfunction is taken to be the norm and good health the exception. Relief from the multitudinous ailments is possible only through using a variety of popular pills, liquids, salves, and special foods.

For people who are easily persuaded that they have some illness or symptom of physical distress, television offers a wide and continuous choice of symptoms. After an evening of being bombarded directly and indirectly, the average viewer is very conscious of his head, breath, teeth, bowels, skin, and degree of tension.

Through television commercials and such programs as soap operas and medically-oriented series, people are actually encouraged to "think sick." It is because of the effectiveness of television that top advertisers spent more than two billion dollars in television advertising during 1969—a figure that goes up each year.

Television panders to the individual who wants to be the center of attention through some minor illness. He can watch commercials and programs and then unconsciously select the illness that most appeals to him at that time or best suits his emotional needs.

The best cure for the television-induced psychosomatic illness is a simple finger-wrist exercise—turning a knob or pushing a button. When the television set is off, so are the opportunities it presents for picking up new ailments.

This is not to say that all television is bad. But it is axiomatic that hours spent staring at a mechanical device will do nothing for your latent creativity or your health. Television, if viewed with discretion and some degree of selectivity, can have its place in your leisure-time activities. Used wisely, it can help to develop your ideas and stimulate your thinking. This, in turn, is a factor in keeping you feeling fit and healthy.

Making Work Out of Play

There are many people who don't know how to play. They do not understand the part that play should have in their lives. And that is because they do not understand the psychology behind regression.

Regression is returning to a more childlike state of mind and emotions, as well as more childlike actions. It happens whenever you take time to relax, play a game, or indulge in some form of humor. The person who goes out to play golf or tennis, the busy man who stops and goes fishing, the housewife who goes to a matinee or spends an afternoon playing bridge, all are taking needed time for relaxation.

But the person who makes work out of play soon develops a compulsive and rigid personality. He forgets how to laugh, how to relax and enjoy life. The pursuit of leisure-time activities with great seriousness and intensity suggests a personality deficiency and some related emotional problems. And these emotional problems can be reflected in a variety of psychosomatic symptoms.

The "golf-score ulcer" is a common psychosomatic illness that afflicts people who are unable to take leisure as it should be taken—as a time for relaxation and enjoyment. They will not accept the premise that there are times when a person should "let himself go" and act freely. They rarely have a good time at parties or other social gatherings because they can't unbend. Frequently, their attitude toward relaxation becomes so rigid that they take refuge in psychosomatic illnesses rather than attempt to cope with leisure situations.

Al was a busy executive who nevertheless took time out for sports. He played tennis and golf. Unfortunately, he carried over into those games the same ruthless, competitive spirit he displayed in business. The result was that he became very nervous, and developed an ulcer and chronic indigestion. In addition, he had difficulty finding golf and tennis partners, since few people cared for his highly aggressive attitude. When his doctor suggested that he take his games less seriously, Al was outraged. "I play to win—that's all that counts!" was his statement.

Not until he was hospitalized with a severe attack of fatigue and bleeding ulcers was Al willing to concede that his "leisure" was contributing to his poor health. His family doctor suggested that he get psychiatric counseling.

Psychoanalysis revealed that Al's determination to win at everything came from an attitude he had developed during his adolescence.

"We were a poor family," he explained. "This didn't seem to matter too much when I was a child and we lived in the country. Then we moved to the city when I was in high school, and I was an object of humor and scorn because my clothes weren't like those the other kids had. In addition, I had no money for textbooks, which had to be supplied by the students themselves, and the lunches which I brought from home were nothing like those of the other kids. After being laughed at, I decided that the only way to get ahead in the world was to become outstanding in everything I did. By the time I graduated from high school I was still poor, but nobody made fun of me anymore because I was a star athlete."

Although Al no longer had to fear the laughter of his peers, he could not let down for a moment. He still felt that the only way he would be accepted by others was to excel at everything.

He was now at an age and a level in business and society when he should have been able to relax and enjoy his leisure. And as everyone does, he needed the positive benefits of recreation for his health.

Gradually, Al was able to change his attitude and loosen up a bit. He stopped demanding of himself that he win every game he played, and started concentrating on having a pleasant time. It was suggested to him that instead of trying to beat all the other players, he spend some of his time helping them to improve their skills.

After two years, Al admitted that his scores at tennis

and golf were no longer the best in his group, but he had helped others raise their scores. Most important, his physical symptoms and nervousness were gone.

Knowing when to use regression, a return to less mature forms of behavior, is, paradoxically, an aspect of maturity. There are appropriate times for laughter and fun. If you cannot learn to balance your time so that you have several hours a week for play, you are building yourself into a box. If you feel that you are too dignified or important to relax or have fun, then you are nailing a lid on that box!

Perhaps you are one of those individuals who feels compelled to work hard constantly. If this is the case, ask yourself if you are really running away from something. What do you think would happen if you stopped working and started using your free time in a constructive and useful fashion?

Take some time to analyze the possible reasons for your compulsion to work hard and ignore the benefits of leisure. One man, for example, discovered that he drove himself to the point of exhaustion because he was literally afraid to stop. He had a psychological fear of facing himself and his personal problems.

As long as he kept busy, he did not have to think about his attitudes, his past, the consequences of any decision, or the dissatisfaction with himself and his life that he secretly felt. And although he complained a great deal about his chronic fatigue and even admitted that it was probably shortening his life, he could not change the pace of his life.

There is an old folk saying that "hard work never killed anyone," but that is fallacious. Hard work has killed plenty of people and will continue to do so as long as people are not able to alternate work and rest periods.

The Real Meaning of Restlessness

Restlessness is a physical symptom of emotional anxiety. The restless person does not use his leisure for relaxation because he is unable to relax. Restlessness starts in the mind, spreads outward to the body, and is shown in a variety of physical or motor ways. The restless individual may become a compulsive talker or use gestures or perform actions which are energy-consuming but meaningless in themselves. The restless person usually is unable to sit still for any length of time and has trouble concentrating on one project or idea.

The restless person also suffers from chronic fatigue and other psychosomatic illnesses, such as headaches, muscle spasms, itching, and gastrointestinal disturbances. Always "on the go," he never really gets rested or relaxed.

One woman told me that her husband, Sam, was extremely restless and that it was breaking up their marriage. "He seems to have a lot of energy, but he never gets anything finished," she complained. "He starts one project, drops it for another one, and then drops that for a third one, and so on. He has insomnia and can't seem to get relaxed enough to get a full night's sleep. As a result of this sleeplessness, he doesn't eat as he should and he keeps losing weight."

She went on to say that in fifteen years of married life, they had moved thirteen times; Sam never was satisfied to stay in one place very long. He also was a "job hopper" and rarely stayed at a job for more than a year. Her experience with his restlessness was making her extremely nervous.

I asked what Sam did with his leisure time, and she said his leisure time was like the rest of his life—a restless hit-and-miss matter of trying something one day and discarding it the next. "Our house is full of hobby kits, woodworking tools, even a loom," she said. "He becomes very enthusiastic about a hobby, rushes out and buys equipment, uses it once or twice, and then takes up something else. Just last week he bought an expensive camera, but he is already talking about taking up bicycling for a hobby!"

What caused Sam's restlessness? Behind his rushing around was a kind of mindless panic. Sam suffered from anxiety and tension which in his case was expressed through restlessness, insomnia, and loss of appetite. The anxiety he felt came from almost overwhelming insecurity. Sam feared failure, and because of this fear, he never completed any job or task or continued with a hobby. As long as he did not finish anything, he would never have to face the possibility of failure.

When, through psychoanalysis, Sam developed a sense of personal esteem and security, he was able to sleep, his appetite returned and his restlessness diminished. When I last heard from him he had been at the same job for four years. He was buying a house, and his marriage was a happy one. He had also kept up the same hobby, photography, for three years and was still enthusiastic about it. He had made a pattern of small but significant successes in his own life.

Constructive Uses of Your Leisure Time

Relaxation and play are constructive uses of your leisure time and are vital to your physical and mental well-being. You have the responsibility for deciding how you are going to spend your leisure time and what effect it is going to have on your life.

To be most beneficial, leisure time must in some way add to your personality. It should be a time of mature regression from which you emerge refreshed and renewed. It should also provide creative stimulus and possibilities for your continued growth as a human being.

Constructive use of leisure will help you get over some of your psychosomatic illnesses. Many people who complain of being too sick or tired to do anything find that the right leisure activity or hobby works a miraculous cure for them. Poor use of leisure time leads to boredom, and boredom leads to psychosomatic illness.

Leisure time can be used to compensate for areas of frustration in your life. Instead of moping over unsatisfactory events, you can use your leisure time to increase your store of happiness.

You have control over your free hours, so why not make the most of them? There is an infinite variety of things to do in your leisure time. You should select an activity that is most suitable to your interests and needs. Your life will not only be more enjoyable, but you will become a more attractive person. If you had the choice of being one or two people—one who does nothing in his spare time and is dull, bored, and full of complaints about ailments or one who uses his leisure time wisely and whose personality sparkles with enthusiasm, friendliness, and good health—which person would you choose to be? Of course you would choose the second person, so why not start now to learn to be the person of your choice?

Understanding Your Skin Problems

Skin: Your Emotional Indicator

One time I asked a group of preschool children what they thought of skin and whether or not it was useful. One little boy said that skin was "to keep your insides from falling out," and another child defined skin as "what keeps your bones covered up." A little girl thought for a minute and then stated that skin was "a kind of plastic that keeps you from getting wet and cold inside." One boy remarked sagely that skin "get scratches and marks but it gets well and is just like new."

All of the children agreed that without skin, there wouldn't be much to a person. In fact, the idea of no skin sent them into convulsions of laughter as they pictured the person who had flesh and bones but no covering for them.

Of course we know that people cannot live without skin; this is one of the problems with severe burn injury cases. What was amusing to the children can become a chilling and frightening experience to the person who suffers a traumatic injury involving skin loss.

Skin is more than necessary to us, however; it is also an emotional indicator. It reflects our feelings. It provides us with certain sensual reactions and experiences. Thus, through our skin we feel sensations of hot or cold, pain and pressure. And as we shall see in this chapter, we feel such related sensations as tingling, itching, and perspiring, which are physical responses to emotional reactions.

In addition, the skin changes color because of emotional conditions. You have doubtless experienced such responses yourself or seen them happen to other people. An individual becomes pale when overcome by anxiety or fear. Anger, embarrassment, or stress can turn a person's face red and cause excessive perspiration. In fact, there are many common folk expressions which relate to change in skin condition or color: "Was my face red when I found out that. . . ." "When he heard the news, he turned absolutely white!" and "It was such a scary movie that it made my skin crawl!"

As a means of communication, skin often reveals what we are trying to hide. The person who receives bad or startling news and says it doesn't matter will fool no one if his face has turned pale.

In addition, a chronic emotional condition is often reflected in the skin's condition and color. The depressed person frequently has a pallor which sets him apart from others. The nervous person may exhibit signs of pimples, eczema, or other skin rashes. The irritated or constantly angry person will have a flushed or red face.

Hives: A Call for Comforting and Cuddling

Hives, which are raised white areas surrounded by reddish itchy patches, can occur on any part of the body. They can be large or small in size. Also known as urticaria, hives are an allergic condition which can be traced to emotional causes.

Hives are seemingly caused by certain foods, clothing, climate, or other environmental conditions. As with all psychosomatic illnesses, these are the apparent or surface causes. The real cause is usually hidden—anxiety, nervous depression, fears, guilt feelings, or other emotional reactions.

Hostility is one of the most common causes of hives. In this case, the skin is expressing the anger and aggression that you repress. One man, for example, suffered from hives only when he visited his wife's family. Although he jokingly suggested that it might be the family that caused his hives, he insisted that in reality it was the change in water and climate. Through analysis he faced the fact of repressed hostility toward his in-laws, hostility which had begun when they had been opposed to his marrying into the family. When he realized that they no longer had this feeling toward him, he was able to accept them as they had accepted him, and he could visit them without being afflicted with hives.

That case seems rather obvious even to an untrained observer, but not all cases are so simple. One patient, Mr. N., suffered from hives at least once a month. He finally ascribed these attacks to "dust in the atmosphere" at the office. A visit to the office did not reveal any unusual concentration of dust, so it was clear that there must have been some other reason for his attacks of hives. He admitted that he did not always get hives when he was in the office, and sometimes when he had been there for only a few minutes. "It just drives me crazy," he said, "I can't do my work because of the itching. I'm even thinking of changing jobs."

A salesman, Mr. N. spent most of his time on the road, but at least once a month he had to spend a day or two in the office doing paperwork. Investigation revealed that he did not like desk work and preferred to be out meeting people and selling his products. He felt annoyed and unhappy at being forced to spend time in the office. Hives were the way he unconsciously chose to express that annoyance.

When Mr. N. realized that his hives would occur if he had to work in any office, he changed his plans to give up his job. He made himself accept this part of his work and the fact that he would have to spend some time in the office. Later, he was able to report that he had only occasional attacks of hives, and those when he was under some pressure to get reports and accounts finished.

What Mr. N. and millions like him are actually in need of are understanding, comforting, and sympathy. Mr. N. really wanted his boss to feel sorry for him, to understand how difficult it was for him to be inside, and to excuse him from doing that part of his work. This is the same kind of emotional reasoning that makes Johnny break into hives when faced with a difficult and unwelcome school problem. He wants the comfort of understanding parents and teachers and the assurance that he will not have to try to cope with that problem.

Mary blamed her hives on a food allergy, and as a result, she refused to dine out or attend social functions where food was served. Analysis revealed that her "allergy" was a lack of self-confidence in social situations and low self-esteem. She wanted to be liked, especially by men, but she did not feel that her personality would attract them. Hives became her excuse for not risking unpopularity. When, through treatment, her self-esteem was raised, Mary was able to go out, have a good time, eat whatever was served, and not have hives.

The child or the adult who feels unloved, who wants to be "cuddled," will frequently have hives. In a sense, he is insisting that he be given care and consideration. I know of one case in which the only caressing a child received from his indifferent mother was when he broke out in a rash and she had to rub some ointment on his body. Hives are the skin's way of crying.

Hives, like other skin ailments and psychosomatic symptoms, are a socially acceptable way of avoiding feared or unpleasant situations. Recently, I met a friend who had been reluctantly planning a trip to take care of some family business. When I asked him how the trip had gone, he said, "Oh, I didn't get to go because I broke out in such hives that by the time I recovered the matter had been taken care of by some other relatives."

If you have hives, you should look into the possible connection between your emotions and your skin condition. Blaming your affliction on food or exterior circumstances will not cure you, but learning the interior reasons for it may.

The Unlovable Lizard

"No one could love me," cried a woman patient, "Look, my skin is so scaly that I'm about as lovable as a lizard!"

Her skin was dry and scaly. This skin condition had started when her husband left her for another woman. In trying to find reasons for the breakup of her marriage, she finally concluded that she was too unattractive to succeed in marriage. And, as if to bear out her conclusion, she developed a skin problem.

Although she was unhappy and uncomfortable with her itchy, scaly skin, it seemed better than admitting that her husband preferred to live with someone else. At the same time, she was building up a barrier to keep people away so that she would not again suffer such a blow to her emotions and pride.

Sometimes the person with dry, patchy, scaly skin has so little self-esteem that he deliberately neglects himself. He unconsciously takes a sort of pleasure in suffering and being uncomfortable because he has conditioned himself to feel valueless as a person. The sight of his scaly skin reaffirms to him that he is indeed unworthy and unlovable. By not taking care of his skin, he is saying to the world at large, "I'm nothing!"

Any kind of skin rash can come from nervousness or tension, guilt or frustration. Jack was being considered for a promotion, and during that time he developed neurodermatitis. The thick, itchy patches which appeared on his arms and neck were a source of great embarrassment to him. He blamed the starch in his shirts for the condition, but after he received his promotion, his neurodermatitis disappeared.

One acquaintance told me that when he had been in school he always suffered from a kind of nervous eczema at examination time. "I knew what was causing it," he said, "but at that time I didn't know enough about coping with stress situations. The same pattern started when I had my first job, but I made up my mind not to let tension take over my life."

His formula for coping with his eczema and the tension that caused it was to have an absorbing hobby to which he could turn in his free time.

"That relaxes me," he explained, "and I stop thinking about my problems. There are times when I come home from work tense and worried and with an itching sensation all over my body. I go into my workshop and start one of my woodworking projects, and pretty soon I'm free of all tension and all my itching."

Joan developed neurodermatitis during the first months of her pregnancy. Her attitude toward motherhood was ambivalent. On the one hand, she wanted the baby, but on the other hand, she resented the changes that would come about in her life. The conflict she felt was expressed in her skin.

She also admitted that she had always thought that pregnant women were ungainly and ugly. Her neurodermatitis served to reinforce her idea of ugliness, as well as to increase her discomfort. It was only after she was able to accept her pregnancy in a positive way that her neurodermatitis cleared.

Your skin speaks to you and to the world. If you have "alligator skin" or any form of neurodermatitis, it is usually because you want to express ugliness in yourself. This may not be a conscious wish at all, but it is nevertheless a projection of your personality.

Salves, ointments, and other treatments can give you only the "temporary relief" so popular with radio and television commercials. But you deserve to have more than temporary relief from your skin problems. Skin disorders are like any other psychosomatic disease—they are unnecessary!

One of the most difficult things to do is to ask yourself that important question. Why do I want to look ugly? Is it a question of low self-esteem or lack of personal self-confidence? Your skin trouble may very well be the outward indication of some hidden emotional trouble. Guilt may be the real dominating factor in your skin disease. There are many instances in which people who have feelings of guilt cannot stand the emotional burden of that guilt and exhibit some psychosomatic symptom which symbolizes it.

One patient with psoriasis denied that there was any emotional connection. Later, however, he admitted that the onset of his psoriasis coincided with an extramarital love affair. "I know I am guilty and would be despised by my wife if she knew," he said. "No one ever found out about my affair, and I broke it off. I know I should be punished, but I just can't come out and confess what I have done."

This insistence on punishment fit in with his strong religious convictions and made it mandatory that he unconsciously punish himself. In his own words, "By being unfaithful to my wife, everything turned ugly inside me. I'm rotten inside!"

That self-condemnation of "rottenness" found its outlet in psoriasis.

Sexual Implications of Skin Disorders

Through psychoanalytical studies a number of psychological and emotional conditions have been found to be connected with skin disorders. Some of these conditions are sexual in their origin. Researchers have found that skin diseases can be traced to exhibitionism, narcissism, masochism, and hostile sexual feelings.

Rectal itch as well as itching and irritation of the vagina are among the most common skin complaints. Since scratching these body areas is not considered permissible in society, afflicted patients are in misery and are constantly seeking some form of relief. Again, although large sums of money can be spent on various salves, lotions, and other patent medicines, the only cure is the discovery and treatment of the particular emotional problem causing the symptom.

It is difficult to generalize about this kind of itching, since there are a number of psychological causes. However, as a result of many case studies, I can suggest some recurring causes. One is guilt over sex. This does not have to be guilt over sexual acts, but can be over sexual thoughts. Frequently, cases of vaginal and anal itching are found in unmarried women and men who have strong guilt feelings about natural eroticism and interest in sexual matters. The itching is the outward expression of the inner conflict they are suffering over their sexual curiosity.

Itching (pruritus) of the rectal or sexual organs can also be a substitute for masturbation. The scratching of the affected parts provides erotic pleasure and sexual satisfaction, and at the same time, the individual fools himself into thinking that he is not indulging in sexual activity. A strong conflict regarding sex is sometimes temporarily resolved by scratching. There can be no guilt if there is no obvious sexual intention—such is the reasoning in these cases.

Skin disease, including pruritus, is also found in individuals who have exhibitionistic tendencies. Scratching is a way of calling attention to themselves and their bodies, and the lesions that may be formed may be exhibited to others. The individual is seeking attention, and he literally forces other people to notice him because of his skin condition. Most of us, in one way or another, use our bodies to attract attention. However, unlike the normal behavior pattern of selecting certain types of clothing or otherwise trying to enhance one's appearance, the emotionally sick person uses a negative way of asking for attention.

Closely allied to the individual who "enjoys" displaying the scars and lesions of skin diseases is the individual who tattoos his skin. This is frank exhibitionism. The tattooed person knows that he is going to cause other people to look at him. And the more tattoos he has or the more outrageous the tattoos, the more notice he is going to get.

Many of the pictures, signs, or symbols used in tattooing the skin are phallic in nature. Some of the favorite devices used, such as daggers, snakes, and eagles are also sexual symbols. For example, the man who has a dagger tattooed on his arm is saying symbolically, "Look at what a big and powerful penis I have!"

The individual with the tattoos and the individual with psoriarsis or other skin disease may realistically be said to be "brothers under the skin." The sexual motivations in such cases are similar, but the expression of them varies. A person of a certain social standing is not going to get himself tattooed, but he or she can get a disease. By suffering from an "allergy," one is assured of getting attention as well as a certain amount of sympathy.

If you have any skin problems you should always consider the possibility of hidden sexual motivations or conflicts as the cause.

The Aggravation of Acne

Acne occurs more frequently during adolescence. It is a mistaken belief, however, that it is an inevitable part of adolescence. Acne during adolescence is usually attributed to various causes but they are usually convenient pegs rather than real causes. Diet is often blamed as the culprit, as is dirty skin, but as conclusions they are erroneous. Diet and dirt may play a part, since they influence the general health of the individual. In addition, a diet rich in starches and greasy foods can make an oily skin become more oily, and if the skin is not kept clean, dirt gets into the open, oily pores; the result can be pimples and other skin blemishes. But what causes oily skin? During adolescence there is an increase in oily secretion. This is a physiological change, one of the many body changes during adolescence. However, there are numerous psychological changes during this same period, too, and their emotional effects can cause acne.

The main cause of adolescent acne is masturbatory guilt. During early adolescence there is a tremendous amount of fluctuating sexual excitement which produces such sudden bodily changes as sweating and an increase in blood flow. This highly changeable emotional state results in blushing and overactivity of the oil glands of the face. (There is an old folk saying that "your guilt shows on your face," and for many young people this is the case). Since overt sexual activity by adolescents is usually frowned upon by parents and society in general, much of the sexual excitement of adolescence is satisfied through masturbation. But masturbation is often accompanied by feelings of guilt, and the guilt finds an outlet in skin disorders.

Many adolescents then add to their skin problems because they persist in scratching the affected areas, or they refuse to take proper hygienic care of their skin.

The best advice for adolescents who suffer from acne is to reach an understanding of their sexual drives and know how to handle these new, unexpected impulses. Understanding plus good personal hygiene should solve most adolescent skin problems.

Pimples are not only found in adolescents, however. Other age-groups can be subject to the same type of skin condition. Again, this may be due to faulty personal habits or to some organic condition, but more often the cause is a sexual excitement and guilt akin to that experienced during adolescence.

Edith, a woman in her early fifties, had a constant problem with pimples. She was an emotionally insecure person who still lived at home with her parents. Although she was a bookkeeper who went to work each day in a large office, she was basically still living in a dependent adolescent situation. Her curiosity and concern about sexual matters were similar to those of an overly emotional and uninformed teen-ager. Forced to live a life devoid of both romantic and sexual opportunities, Edith's only outlet for her normal sexual impulses and fantasies was through masturbation. As a chronic masturbator, Edith knew that she was doing something of which her parents would disapprove, yet she had to have some way of expressing herself. As a result of this conflict, she carried a heavy burden of guilt.

Curing her skin condition was dependent upon changing her situation. After she learned to assert herself and live her own life, Edith's pimples disappeared. Although Edith insisted that being relieved of her affliction seemed like a miracle, the fact was that it had occurred because she had finally reached maturity. Edith had become an adult after a very prolonged adolescence!

Masochism and Aggression in Skin Disorders

In some cases of skin problems there are masochistic elements. Although he may not realize it, the afflicted person may actually enjoy the pain and discomfort he gets from scratching. He is, in a very real sense, injuring himself by his actions. Though some patients have been told that they must not scratch the affected areas or their condition will worsen, they cannot resist scratching. In fact, they may continue until the skin reaches a point where weeping and bleeding occur, followed by infection of the area.

One woman who had an eczematous condition of the neck and scalp was repeatedly told that she must refrain from touching and scratching. Yet she scratched at her head almost constantly until she had lost most of her hair and had a severe infectious condition. She admitted that scratching was painful and that she was fully aware of the consequences. Through psychoanalytic treatment, she was able to admit that she found the sensation of pain very pleasurable.

Raised by strict parents, she had had an unhappy childhood and some traumatic experiences. One repressed experience which analysis brought out was of being punished by her parents when they discovered that she was masturbating. After that she developed an itching condition on her scalp. Emotionally and psychologically, she had simply substituted the hair on her head for her pubic hair and unconsciously transferred her sexual feelings to her head. Yet this substitution still demanded some kind of punishment, so she scratched enough to cause herself pain.

A well-known expression is "itching for a fight," and it describes the kind of aggressive personality who may not only display hostility but may have a psychosomatic illness as well. His hostility and aggressive impulses may be manifested in a red, mottled complexion or a crusted and scabious skin.

Anger can also cause a rash or other skin conditions to occur. This is especially true if the anger is repressed.

Other kinds of repressed emotion can produce a skin condition. Babies and children with skin diseases often have the double handicap of not being loved by their mothers and not being properly cared for physically. The same thing can happen to adults. Mrs. S. had an itching rash over most of of her body. She blamed soap and water, and had gotten to a point where she refused to bathe. Her neglected physical condition was a reflection of her marital problems. She felt unloved by her husband and unwanted by her parents, who had forced her into marriage after she became pregnant. The pregnancy had ended in a miscarriage, but her emotional damage remained. By the time she sought medical help, her physical and mental conditions were such that she had alienated most of her friends.

This was was a case where counseling was needed for an entire family before the skin condition could be cured. Fortunately for Mrs. S., she was living in a city where there was a clinic which could care for her emotional and physical needs. With the help of trained counselors, she and her husband were able to make a fresh start in their marriage. Mrs. S.'s parents were persuaded to stop their recriminations and overcome the hostility which had started the family trouble.

Although we have been talking primarily about skin conditions of the face or entire body, dermatitis may be very localized. In localized cases, the cause usually narrows down to a specific emotional need or problem. A man with a skin disorder of his eyelids was frustrated in his work, and in his words, "sick of seeing the same old faces every day!" His way of dealing with his emotional conflict was to develop this skin condition. Another person in the same situation might have developed hysterical blindness. A change in jobs took care of his eyelid dermatitis.

In another case, a man with a nagging wife developed otitis externa, a skin condition affecting the external part of the ear. What he was expressing was the desire to become deaf to his wife's voice.

While some people may have extremely sensitive skin and are unable to tolerate soaps and washing powders, many cases of dermatitis blamed on those products may have emotional causes. The wife who cannot wash dishes because her hands break out in a rash may be showing dissatisfaction with her marriage. The real irritation is not on her skin but in her life.

Many people use the possibility of skin irritation as an excuse to avoid what they dislike or fear. One woman would not take on any hobbies that required the use of her hands because she claimed that her skin was so sensitive that she had to be careful what she touched or handled. The emotional reason behind her skin "allergy" was her fear of not being able to succeed in what she attempted to do. Success was all-important to her, and since she had little manual dexterity, she was afraid to try things with her hands. Her self-esteem generally was so low that she could not risk failure in any aspect of her life.

A man who had been raised on a farm and disliked the long hours and hard work developed an allergy to dirt when he became an adult. Whenever he worked out in the yard, he would get red, itchy bumps on his hands.

Our Need for "Touch-Love" and Its Relationship to Our Skin Allergies

One of the important sensations connected with the skin is the sensation of touch. Touch (or pressure) utilizes the nerve endings in the skin. These nerve endings vary so that some parts of the body are more responsive to touch or pressure than other parts. The hands, for example, are more sensitive than the legs or back.

We need this sense of touch in our lives, both when we touch other objects and other people, and when we ourselves are touched. When we touch, we are using and experiencing perception. When we are touched, we know that we have become an experience of perception to someone. This builds up our self-esteem.

Touch is one form of interpersonal communication that breaks all barriers between people. Differences in age, education, beliefs, nationalities, and language melt away under touching.

The baby lives in a tactile world. Through the medium of touch he experiences love, security, exploration, joy, and under certain conditions, his first contacts with pain and sorrow. But as the baby grows and matures he develops his other senses, and the tactile expression of his world and thoughts becomes less important. Yet there always remains the desire to be hugged, cuddled, and touched and to be able to touch other people. This desire may be repressed in adults who become rigid in their contacts with others. Their inability to give, receive, or communicate through physical touching symbolizes an inner or emotional rigidity. But because the need remains, there may be a psychosomatic reaction.

We have already spoken of the child who received care and attention from his mother only when he developed a body rash; but an adult may also develop a skin condition in an unconscious attempt to get the touching care he craves.

Vernon had an unhappy childhood and a lonely time as an adult. His mother had been neglectful and disinterested in him as a child. This lack of interest carried over, and Vernon had little contact with his family once he left home. His family experience had made him wary of contact with others, and he was unable to make friends easily. Although he would have liked to meet women and have dates, he was unable to unbend enough to make the first necessary overtures.

Somewhere inside the stoic facade of the adult was the baby Vernon crying to be loved and cuddled. His cry found expression in the form of a skin rash which he blamed on a food allergy. Vernon's allergy was not to food, as he thought, but to loneliness. To go to the doctor, to get treatments and have lotions smoothed on his skin was a way of satisfying that crying inside, but it was not the solution he needed. As an adult, Vernon needed to have a meaningful relationship with another person in which his desire to be loved and touched could be satisfied.

When Vernon was helped through counseling to break out of his shell and make those first tentative steps toward other people, he also experienced some alleviation of his skin condition. Later, as he improved in his ability to meet people, make friends, and have contacts with women, his "allergy" completely disappeared.

In other cases, not wanting to be touched (which usually conceals a hidden desire to be touched) makes a person develop a skin disease. They fear being touched, and their reasoning is that if their skin condition is objectionable, it will keep people at a distance.

I also knew of one woman who immediately stepped

back if anyone tried to touch her hands or arms. "Please don't touch me!" she would exclaim. "I have very sensitive skin and I'll get a rash." This woman was unusually vulnerable emotionally, and very easily hurt. She had already been divorced twice because she could not get along with her husbands. Her skin trouble was an attempt to keep people at arm's length.

You need to feel free to reach out to people and touch them in a friendly, loving, and concerned way and to accept those same touching gestures from others. We all need to touch and be touched, to be warm and affectionate with other people. Don't be too stiff or unfriendly. Don't be afraid to shake hands, to hug or kiss a close friend or family member. An affectionate gesture means more than words.

Remember that dogs are popular, particularly with the lonely and friendless, because they have no hesitation about touching people. They will lick, nuzzle, and paw at people, and they want to be petted in return.

In psychological treatment we now have encounter groups, or sensitivity training sessions. These are group therapy sessions in which people are encouraged to respond to each other in a number of ways, including touching. This touching of hands and bodies results in a breaking down of self-imposed barriers. It also brings out people's hidden and repressed thoughts and emotions. Touching in group therapy has not only brought people into contact with others, but has also served as an exercise in self-confrontation.

However, you don't need to join such a group to get the benefits of touching in your life; you have only to make that first gesture and be willing to accept a returning touch gesture from another person.

Understanding Your Skin Condition

Skin diseases are psychophysiologic disorders, and one must treat both the underlying emotional cause and the affected physical area.

It is impossible to ignore skin trouble—you are re-

minded of its existence every time you look in the mirror or
at your body. Skin trouble of any kind not only makes you
feel bad physically but emotionally as well, because nobody
likes to know that he looks "scruffy."

Accepting the association between emotional problems
and skin problems is the first step in getting lasting relief
from your uncomfortable and unsightly skin condition.

The second step is to correct the conditions that are
causing your emotional problems. Understanding that in
many cases your skin problems come from within, your
mind will help you cope with this type of psychosomatic illness.

IX

Problems Related to Sexual Maturity

Despite All the Jokes, It's a Serious Matter

Although there are many jokes about male impotence and female frigidity, they are serious subjects to the people concerned. It's not very funny to be the impotent man or his wife, and there is nothing humorous about an unresponsive woman, either to her or her partner.

Reliable statistics on the number of cases of impotence and frigidity are not easily found. It has been estimated that about forty percent of men may suffer from impotence at some time in their lives. It is more difficult to compile accurate statistics about women, since many frigid women do not seek medical assistance, psychological counseling, or other forms of help. Nor do women always have an awareness of their own sexual problems. The effects of impotence are more readily seen in the man, whereas a frigid woman may go through her entire married life and not realize that she has a sexual problem. She will feel dissatisfied, but she may have been educated not to expect anything more from sex, or she simply may not understand the role of sex in her unhappiness.

There can be organic causes for lack of sexual response, but ninety percent of all cases of male impotence and female frigidity can be traced to emotional or psychological causes. The individual is usually not aware of the real causes of his or her lack of sexual response. Those causes may lie deeply buried within the subconscious. This inability to respond sexually is another form of psychosomatic response.

As with all illnesses or symptoms, the first step is to determine that there is no physical or organic cause. Once that has been established, the next step is to seek out the psychological cause and treat it.

Sexual dysfunction is no different from any other body dysfunction, yet until recent years people have had a hush-hush attitude toward it, particularly in regard to problems of women's sexual adjustment. Books, especially those written for lay people, did not discuss the subject candidly but only hinted at possible causes and cures. In many volumes, the whole problem was regarded as a question of morality.

Later in this chapter I will discuss in more detail the psychological effects of this traditional view of sexuality.

The Cold War at Home

Sexual failure is a serious matter for the individual. It is devastating to a marriage.

Sex researchers Dr. William H. Masters and Virginia E. Johnson estimated from their studies at the Reproductive Biology Research Foundation in St. Louis that about 50 per cent of the married couples in the United States fail to have an adequate sexual life.

An inadequate sexual life among the married usually leads to other marital difficulties, ranging from large problems to a number of minor irritations. In time, the problems may become so overwhelming that a divorce is sought, but in most marriages husband and wife, filled with disenchantment, become contestants or outright combatants in a *very* cold war.

"My husband is stingy," complained Mrs. G. "He's gotten so he's very economy-minded and doesn't want to give me anything!"

As it developed in treatment, the quarrels about money between Mrs. G. and her husband were not the real cause for their marriage being on such shaky ground; money had become a symbol for something else—sex. This financial problem had started after Mr. G. had begun to avoid sexual intercourse. Searching for some matter on which to fault him, Mrs. G. picked on money.

All lines of meaningful communication between the couple had broken down, beginning with their failure to communicate sexually. Once the question of sexual failure had been brought into the open, I asked Mrs. G., "Have you discussed this with your husband?" Her reply was, "Oh, I couldn't do that!"

Yet she could and did nag him unmercifully about money matters, and on occasion she even discussed his supposed stinginess with friends and relatives. She was actually unaware that she was using money as a substitute for speaking her mind about sexual matters. What she meant when she said her husband would not give her any money was that he would not give her any sexual satisfaction. She was unaware of this, however; it was a feeling in her subconscious.

Mr. G. was no better able to communicate his true feelings. He too preferred to quarrel over money rather than the actual cause of their marital unhappiness.

Both Mr. and Mrs. G. had to accept treatment and learn to communicate with each other. When they did, Mr. G. was finally able to admit that after a couple of incidents in which he had had difficulty in having an erection, he had fears of becoming sexually inadequate. He preferred to accept the onus of being thought stingy rather than being considered less than the man he had been.

Once Mr. G. was able to discuss his fears, he began to feel more relaxed. This in turn led to a willingness to discuss sexual matters with his wife. Mr. G.'s occasional impotency proved to be a temporary result of extreme tiredness. The quarrels over money ceased, as they now found that money was not an issue between them. Best of all, the G.'s had discovered that they could talk things over without becoming irritated and angry with each other. By establishing lines of communication and facing the real issue, the G.'s saved their marriage and themselves.

The cold war at home is fought with standard phrases, with subterfuge, and with animosity. "I'm too tired," offered as an excuse for not having sexual intercourse, soon engenders bitterness in the partner. And as bitterness becomes mutual, "I'm too tired" translates into "I'm tired of you."

"Not tonight. I have a headache," has become a standard line in comedy routines, but as we said in the beginning of this chapter, it's not really funny. Sexual expression is a vital form of interpersonal communication in married life.

The Passive Male and His Sexual Responses

It is a myth that all men are aggressive and that this is reflected in their sexual behavior and ability. Some men are aggressive, but others are passive. A passive male will have certain personality characteristics and patterns of behavior which are different from those of the aggressive male. His sexual behavior and habits will reflect that passivity.

A man who feels passive and helpless will not function well as a sexual being. However, a passive man married to an aggressive woman will not necessarily feel that he is a failure sexually. If both partners are satisfied with this reversal of the traditional sex roles, they can have a happy marriage. But if the husband feels, or is made to feel, that he is not adequate sexually, he will have personality problems and an unsatisfactory marriage. The average woman does not want a passive man for a husband, but the realization of what passivity means is frequently not clear until after the marriage ceremony.

"I liked Marvin and so did my folks," one woman said. "He was so polite and gentle. I knew married people who quarreled and were loud with each other, and I thought how wonderful Marvin would be and that there would never be cross words between us. Well, we don't quarrel, and Marvin is still polite and gentle, but that's the whole trouble. He's too gentle! I don't feel like I'm married to a real man! Unless I suggest it, we never have sexual intercourse."

When asked if Marvin was a satisfactory sexual partner, she said he was not. Her chief complaint was that he just didn't seem interested. Here was a case where the passive male was not a suitable marriage partner.

I have personally observed a number of marriages in which the wife gradually assumed a more dominant role as her passive husband became more lethargic about his place as head of the household. This passivity generally extends itself to other areas of family life, and it is not unusual to see the wife assume management of family finances, plan all the family activities, and make the major decisions.

What factors create passivity in a male? He is frequently, though not always, an only child. He has had a childhood in which he has been dominated by his parents, particularly by his mother. The emphasis in his early training has been on obedience, politeness, respect, and quietness. The passive male makes an ideal child from the viewpoint of adults who follow the old idea that "children should be seen and not heard." But this well-behaved, quiet, ideal child does not necessarily grow into a mature, manly adult. If the boy-become-man continues to live at home with his parents (and many do), he will continue to receive praise for his attitudes and personality traits. But if he marries, "He's so good to his mother" does not necessarily mean that he will be good to a wife!

Another reason that a man may be passive is some traumatic shock during childhood which has robbed him of his natural aggressiveness. For example, one patient had developed his attitude of sexual passivity after being exposed to the shock of seeing his parents engaged in sexual intercourse. As we said in Chapter III, the recollection of the primal scene can produce various psychosomatic symptoms and personality disorders, including sexual problems.

Not all children will be traumatized by the primal scene, but the majority of children will be. Children in primitive cultures, however, do not experience the same sense of shock at seeing their parents or other adults engaged in sexual activity that our children do. This is, perhaps, an indictment of our cultural attitude toward sex.

Psychic Causes of Impotence and Frigidity

Most of the actual causes of impotence or frigidity are psychic or emotional in nature. These causes, as in other types of psychosomatic illnesses and symptoms, are frequently unknown to the person because he or she has repressed the memory of the original incident or experience. Other people may be vaguely aware of what in their past experience has been responsible for their present-day feelings, but they cannot rid themselves of the effects of those traumatic experiences. We might well compare those early causes to the albatross which hung around the neck of the Ancient Mariner. Knowing what your particular "albatross" is can help you achieve victory over your psychosomatic illness. But in addition to knowing, you have to be willing and able to make the change from sickness to health. In sexual matters this is often more difficult because of the centuries-old moral code that still surrounds so much of what we say and do about sex. The traditional religious-ethical-moral view has contributed to many of the psychosomatic problems connected with sexual adjustment.

As we mentioned in the previous section, the primal scene may be one cause of sexual maladjustment. A child, unable to fully comprehend what he sees or hears, may become an adult who is the victim of his childhood imagination.

In one case of a sexually frigid woman, it was revealed that as a child she had developed a horror of being touched or fondled in any way after the primal scene became confused in her mind with a television program she had seen in which people were being tortured. She felt sure that her mother was being hurt, and she became afraid that she too might be hurt. Although as an adult she longed to be married, she could not get rid of what she termed her "irrational" fear of being touched, particularly in a sexual way.

Through treatment, she learned that her fear had a cause and a cure. It was an irrational fear in the sense that it could be traced to an experience that did not realistically justify it, and it was irrational also in the sense that it was unnecessary.

Many cases of sexual maladjustment, with their corresponding psychosomatic symptoms, can be traced directly to faulty parental attitudes. The mother who tells her children or implies by her attitude that sex is "nasty" or "dirty" is encouraging them to accept impotence or frigidity as their sexual lots in life.

Impotence can also occur when a man has little self-esteem. His body responds to the mental signal that is saying, "I'm a failure; I'm not much of a man." The man who has the best sexual adjustment is the man who also feels well-integrated as a personality. Because he has high self-esteem and an appreciation of himself as a person of worth, he performs well in all areas of his life, including his sex life. Similarly, a woman who has no concept of her worth as a person will not be able to fully respond sexually.

In the nineteenth century there were many advertisements for patent medicines guaranteed to "restore energy." But there is no remedy or cure that can be accomplished by a pill, an elixir, or tonic. If you have problems that are related to your sexual life, you can be helped if you analyze the probable emotional background of those problems. Knowing why you respond (or fail to respond) as you do can help you change your attitude so that you can have a more satisfactory sex life.

Castration Anxiety

Castration anxiety or castration complex is neither unusual nor mysterious. This anxiety by itself does not indicate an abnormality of personality, as it can simply be an emotional state of mild but constant anxiety. In theory, this anxiety is caused by a male's unconscious fear of being deprived of his sexual organs. In extreme cases, a man may be so affected that he mentally feels as if such a dramatic operation has already taken place, and he tends to behave as if he were, in fact, a castrated male.

It takes a minimum of two persons for a castration complex or anxiety to develop. It may start in childhood with the relationship between mother and child. The mother may suggest to her child that if he is not good, he will be punished, and it is implied that such punishment involves losing his penis. This is usually not done in an obvious and threatening way, but the effect on the child is the same as if it were. Frequently, however, a child is actually told that if he masturbates he will be punished by having his penis removed.

One patient who suffered from castration anxiety remembered being told by his mother that if he continued to act "naughty" he would be taken to the doctor to have his penis cut off. As a result, he developed a childhood fear of doctors. "I remember," he said, "being carried screaming into the doctor's office when I fell out of a tree and broke my arm. I knew that he must know in some way that I had been masturbating, and as a result, he was going to do what my mother kept threatening me with!"

As an adult he had gotten over his fear of doctors, but the castration anxiety remained to plague his life and cause him unhappiness. His views had become more sophisticated, however, and in his private ethical scheme, he had a fear that if he did something wrong, he would be punished by having some disease that affected his penis, or that he would be in an accident which would castrate him. He knew a number of supposedly true and lurid stories of men who had been wounded in the war and lost their sexual organs, of farmers who had fallen on mechanical rakes, of laborers who had been castrated by accidents involving the machines they were working on, and many case histories about men who had developed cancer involving the sexual organs. With analysis and treatment, he was finally able to resolve this anxiety problem.

Castration anxiety may not develop until adulthood, when it often can be traced to the attitude of a wife or other woman who holds some strong emotional position in the life of the affected man. It is not unusual for wives to happily marry and then later complain bitterly that they are disappointed in their husbands, and in particular, in their sexual experiences together. What these women fail to see is that in many cases it is their own fault that their husbands are not sexually adequate partners.

A woman may be a castrating female; that is, she enjoys putting men down. She cuts men down in an intellectual way which is symbolic of an unconscious desire to castrate them. She may unconsciously feel inferior to men because they have a penis and she does not. She may feel that men are worthless and need to be forced into a subordinate position.

A castrating female is usually sarcastic, easily irritated, and often chronically suspicious of other people. She may so dominate her husband that his personality and sexual life diminish to zero, yet she still complains about his lack of ambition in life and his lack of interest in her. A castrating female may have a series of marriages or romantic alliances, yet the result in each one will be negative. She is not satisfied until she does cut the man in her life down to nothing; yet when she succeeds, she no longer wants him. Like the male spider of some species, he is devoured—he has served his purpose.

In such a marriage, the husband who feels castrated becomes impotent. He is responding psychosomatically to the situation.

Female Negative Identification in Sex Roles

When we say that a woman's identification with her sex role is a negative one, we mean that whether she realizes it or not, she considers women to be inferior to men. This negative identification usually comes from parental attitudes.

Women who have negative identifications in their sex roles suffer from a variety of psychosomatic symptoms, not the least of which is difficulty in sexual relations. Considering women to be worthless leads to a negative attitude toward sexual matters. Such an attitude may cause frigidity or feelings of guilt or fear in regard to sexual relations.

To protect themselves from having to have sexual intercourse, women with negative identifications often develop a series of illnesses. They may insist that they are physically unable to participate in the sex act. The real reason is emotional or mental, but they ascribe it to not "feeling well enough." When a woman says to her husband, "I'm too tired," it could really mean, "I'm afraid" or "I'm not happy in my role as a woman."

The actual fear of penetration is very strong in some women, making it impossible for them to respond sexually. This fear develops in childhood or adolescence, and is frequently transmitted by mothers or other adult females. One women told me, "My mother would confide in me when I was an adolescent and tell me how painful intercourse was. She made it out to be a time of suffering and endurance. I always felt that women were unlucky because they had to put up with this if they wanted to get married."

Another woman said she had been frightened by the stories told by a cousin and an aunt about the sizes of men's sexual organs. "They told tales which they swore were true," she said. "One was about a woman who was ruptured by a man with an enormous penis. They described the wedding night as one of severe pain and suffering. I used to have dreams in which a man with a large stick would chase me down a dark street, and I would wake up crying. I knew the significance of the dreams, but I could not get over my fear of being hurt in sexual intercourse. I developed a fear of being raped, and for a long time refused to go out alone at night. I had social problems because I became afraid to date boys. I would go out, but then I would start thinking about the size of their sexual organs and become so nervous that I would get sick and have to go home."

This woman had rationalized her fears to the extent that she decided she could marry a man who was injured in some way or who was an invalid incapable of sexual activity. She wanted the companionship that marriage could offer, but she did not want to risk what she felt was physical danger to her person. While her fears seem childishly immature, they were very real to her. They were preventing her from leading a normal life. They were keeping her from marriage.

In a similar situation, a woman patient developed allergies that kept her from engaging in social activities. In this way she was able to avoid becoming involved with men. She too had a fear of penetration.

Not only fear but hostility in sexual relationships can also occur when a woman has a negative identification with her role as a female. Again, this may come from some childhood episode in which she is made to feel that being a girl is undesirable. From then on, she is filled with conflicting emotions about womanhood. Men become her rivals, and she treats each male-female encounter as if it were a duel rather than a date.

This hostility toward men and toward acceptance of the female role may lie dormant until after marriage. Sometimes the first act of intercourse may be sufficient to arouse repressed feelings of hostility. Unconsciously, the woman desires to take revenge on men, and she does this either by refusing to continue to have sexual intercourse with her husband or by assuming an attitude of indifference or contempt during the sex act.

The emotionally immature woman will also have difficulty in achieving sexual adjustment. She will instead respond to sexual demands, both her own and those of her marriage partner, with various psychosomatic symptoms. She unconsciously regards her husband as a father figure who has taken the place in her life of her actual father. She has a deep devotion to her father but is aware of the prohibition against incestuous relationships. That same prohibition is unconsciously transferred to her husband. She solves her moral dilemma by being too tired or too sick to engage in sex, although she does like to be petted and caressed. She is affectionate, but she wants to be the little girl rather than the wife.

The same thing happens with men who, being overly devoted to their mothers, find that they are impotent with their wives but are able to achieve sexual satisfaction with prostitutes or mistresses.

The Genital Character

It is possible for each person to achieve full sexual maturity. One of the things that keeps people from becoming sexually mature is their inability to progress beyond the oral or the anal stage of their emotional development.

The oral character, as mentioned in Chapter 4, is very infantile in his responses to life situations and to other people. In a sexual situation this infantile behavior means behaving immaturely and unrealistically.

The oral character is often impotent or frigid. He or she is extremely self-centered and unable to give to others in a satisfactory way.

The anal character is also unable to participate fully and completely in a sexual relationship. He becomes impotent, or she becomes frigid, because of this inability to share.

Individuals who do progress from the first stage, the oral, through the second, the anal, and then to the genital stage are able to accept the pleasures and responsibilities of an adult sex life. They have discarded the self-interest and narcissistic qualities of their previous emotional states.

The genital character is less hostile and more receptive to other people. He has a strong sense of personal identity and a high level of self-esteem which permit him to love other people without feeling a sense of personality diminution.

One of the common misunderstandings about sex is caused by a confusion between physical sexual maturity and emotional sexual maturity. They are not the same. A person may have all the adult physical sexual characteristics, with fully developed sexual organs, and yet have a childishly emotional sexual attitude. This combination of physical maturity plus emotional immaturity leads to the formation of various psychosomatic symptoms, including impotence.

Help Yourself to Sexual Maturity

You can help yourself achieve sexual maturity and enjoy greater happiness in your life. You do this by facing the present implications of your sexual problems and deciding to determine the background of your problems. You may require some professional assistance, but it is entirely possible to work out solutions to your problems by yourself.

If impotence, for example, is your psychosomatic sexual problem, you now know that there is a high probability that it has an emotional cause. You may have to go far back into your past to find the root cause. You may have to face the unpleasant fact that you are reacting in a sexually immature way to other people. If your sexual life is not satisfactory, you may have to admit that you may be at fault.

Remind yourself that you are (1) an adult and (2) an adult of personal worth. As an adult with self-esteem, you will naturally behave in certain ways which are more mature and more satisfying than if you were behaving childishly.

Having a healthy attitude toward sexuality means that you have respect for yourself as a person and an understanding of what is required to have a meaningful relationship with another person. "Sexual freedom" does not mean promiscuity, as is popularly thought; it means having a strong sense of positive sexual identity. It means having the capacity to express yourself sexually in a mature and mutually enjoyable relationship: You accept yourself in your sexual role, and you are able to convey to others your acceptance of yourself as a sexual person, without putting undue or unnatural emphasis on sexual matters.

X

Menstruation, Menopause, and Myth

Myths of Menstruation

All body functions are subject to mythological interpretation and wonder. Although this was particularly true in early times when the average lay person knew little about the functions and diseases of his body (and the men of learning know little more), some of the myths and mysteries continue to surround certain body functions. Menstruation is one such function which, although now easily understood in terms of both its physical significance and mental effects, still is thought of by many people in terms of the early myth and superstition. It is for this reason that menstrual problems cause a high proportion of present-day psychosomatic illnesses.

Certainly, to the primitive man and woman, as to the uninformed, menstruation is a disturbing event. Anthropologists studying the customs and mores of primitive tribes have frequently found that menstruation arouses anxiety because its physiological cause and significance is not understood. In some areas, a woman is regarded as "unclean" during this period. She is kept in isolation, usually to be approached only by other women, and never by men of the tribe. Among the Turu in Tanzania even a married woman is separated at this time. She is sent to the home of her mother during her menstrual period and may not be visited even by her husband. Many societies restrict normal coital activities during menstruation, and the custom of isolating menstruating women helps insure that such restrictions are obeyed.

Isolation and the idea that menstruation is unclean has not been confined to primitive peoples, however, but has been accepted among more sophisticated groups as well. The Biblical attitude toward menstruation has often been cited as precedent for such customs and beliefs. For example, in Leviticus 15:19, "And if a woman have an issue, and her issue in her flesh be blood, she shall be put apart seven days: and whosoever toucheth her shall be unclean until the even." There is also prescribed a ritual of cleansing that the

woman is to undergo after her menstrual period has ended:
"And on the eighth day she shall take unto her two turtles,
or two young pigeons, and bring them unto the priest, to
the door of the tabernacle of the congregation. And the
priest shall offer the one for a sin offering, and the other for
a burnt offering; and the priest shall make an atonement for
her before the Lord for the issue of her uncleanness"
(Leviticus 15:29–30). With this as a background to Western
culture and mores, is it any wonder that traumatic shock
and emotional problems have continued to be associated
with menstruation?

Under the scrutinizing light of modern science and up-
to-date medical and psychological knowledge, many of the
myths surrounding menstruation have been dispelled, yet
some still persist, causing a variety of psychosomatic disorders. One of the most common of those myths is that menstruation must be painful. This myth has been handed down
from one generation of women to another, frequently with
all sorts of embellishments.

Usually it is the mother or other close female relative
who conditions the adolescent girl either to accept, reject, or
fear her menstrual periods. Although there are now available many good books dealing with the onset of the menses
and with the entire menstrual cycle and sexual development
of the woman, people continue to listen to other people, particularly to those with whom they have a close familial or
emotional relationship. If the mother has had a difficult time
adjusting to her menstrual periods, she is going to convey
her anxiety and fear to her daughter.

The most common complaint I have had from women
regarding what other people told them about menstruation
was that they had been led to think of it as painful. One patient said, "I was so frightened by what my mother said
that I wished I could die rather than go through what she
described as 'monthly agony.'" She reported that each
month her mother became very ill and was in bed for at
least two days, during which time the household had to run
itself; she was incapable of doing any work. "I grew up

thinking that this was normal behavior," my patient said.

In her own case, although she did not suffer physical pain and sickness, she became very tense and depressed because she always expected to become incapacitated.

It has also become common to blame the menstrual period for headaches, backaches, irritation, and general feelings of tiredness. Patent-medicine advertisements have contributed to this notion that menstruation automatically means illness. Various pills and tonics are suggested for "those difficult days," or more explicitly, for premenstrual tension, menstrual headaches, nausea, and other related feelings of discomfort. The average girl or woman reading these advertisements is emotionally conditioned to think in terms of discomfort in connection with her monthly period.

Of course, today's advertisements are quite subtle, more attuned to this scientific age than were the advertisements of the nineteenth century which contained such statements as "Painful monthly periods. Congestion of the ovaries, inflammation of the womb, displacements or an impaired nervous system, cause excruciating pain at monthly periods. These pains are alarming symptoms of dangerous derangements." We may laugh at these words, but the same implication can still be found in today's advertisements and attitudes.

Myths about menstruation have been most difficult to dislodge or change because they are connected with all of our ideas about female sexuality and the female's place in the world.

Ambivalence and the Origin of Psychosomatic Menstrual Disorders

Ambivalence is the coexistence of opposing ideas, emotions, or feelings toward another person, an idea, or event. It can be composed of feelings of love-hate, pain-pleasure, kindness-cruelty, or any other form and combination of opposing emotions. Many women have ambivalent feelings toward menstruation. Part of this ambivalence comes from the socio-legal attitudes of the past, which saw women as weaker creatures set apart by their own "peculiarities," including menstruation. This ambivalence causes emotional problems.

To many women menstruation has two aspects. It is a nuisance, an inconvenience, but it also is an affirmation of their essential femininity. These two aspects can become emotionally confused.

Marcella suffered from depression at the onset of her menstrual period. In addition, she frequently had severe cramps and headaches. Her regular doctor could find no organic cause for her symptoms, so he suggested she see a psychiatrist. A successful and busy lawyer, Marcella had ambivalent feelings about many aspects of her life. At the time she came for consultation, she was engaged to be married, but she had not yet set the date.

"I know it's unfair to keep Frank waiting like this," she said, "but I just don't feel sure enough."

"About Frank, or your marriage?"

"No, not about Frank. I really love him, but I do have doubts about combining a career, especially a demanding career like law, with marriage. What if Frank thinks that I should give up my law practice and devote more time to him and to the children we want to have? I'm just not sure what I would feel then or what I really want now."

Treatment revealed that Marcella had confused and anxious feelings about her career and her role as a woman. This was traced directly to parental attitudes which she had tried to suppress. Both Marcella's parents had opposed her choosing law as a career. Her father had said that it was "unfeminine," not suitable for a woman, while her mother had argued that it would make marriage difficult if not impossible. Although she had defied her parents, she could not dismiss their admonitions.

In analysis, she remembered that on several occasions her mother, who had suffered from severe menstrual cramps, had said, "How do you think you will be able to work on the days when you are feeling bad? How can you be a lawyer when once a month you will have to be sick? Everyone will know that you are just a woman!"

Although Marcella had decided that she would not be the kind of person her mother was, she still found, to her dismay and embarrassment, that each month she did become ill.

What Marcella was doing was fighting a civil war within herself. Her monthly periods served to remind her that she was a woman, while her unconscious also reminded her that according to her parents, being a lawyer was unwomanly. While this conflict remained unresolved Marcella suffered menstrual disorders. It was as if her parents were there, saying "I told you so!"

Only when she was able to get over her ambivalence was Marcella cured of her menstrual depression and pain. She had to accept the fact that having a career and being a wife and mother are not necessarily incompatible. As thousands of other people have done, Marcella learned to use her mind and body as one integrated object. She learned that she could indeed be both a successful lawyer and a desirable and very feminine woman.

The Self-Image of the Secondary Citizen—The Female

Without going into all the aspects of the changing attitudes toward women and the liberation of the female citizen both in legal and social terms, let us say that the long-time secondary position of women had an adverse effect upon her emotional health. Now, women are at least legally liberated, despite certain vestiges which remain to cause them some uneasiness. Yet many women still have self-images of themselves as second-class citizens.

A woman who has a poor self-concept will suffer from a variety of psychosomatic illnesses reflecting her own uncertainty and loss of strong personal identity. Because she feels inferior and weak as a woman, she exhibits this in her personal health. It seems most natural for her to suffer from some uniquely feminine disorder; thus she has menstrual problems and related diseases.

Usually, it is parents who first make their girl-children feel that they are less desirable than boys. One woman remembered that she was not permitted to engage in the same physical activities after she had started menstruation. "My mother said that I could no longer play ball and do other things 'at that time,' as she called it. When I asked her why I couldn't do things, while my brother could, she said it was because girls were different, more delicate. She implied that if I continued to engage in sports during my periods, I would have 'trouble.' She also hinted that women who did not take care of themselves not only were in great pain during their periods, but they eventually had to have operations which made them invalids. I was so frightened by my mother's stories that it took years before I would do anything strenuous during my monthly periods. I used to get cramps and feel sick to my stomach just from anxiety."

Another patient with a history of menstrual disorders said that after she started menstruating her father had said, "I would rather shave three times a day with my tender face than have what you are going to have once a month!" Her father's attitude made her feel that she was in some way handicapped. In her own words, "I began to baby my- self, and I expected to feel ill during my period. My father's attitude had convinced me that it was a bad thing and I was somehow at fault for being a girl."

Many women become convinced that it is their preroga- tive to suffer during menstruation, and sometimes this suf- fering conceals a hostility toward men.

Mrs. T. developed menstrual difficulties soon after her marriage. During her monthly period she became nauseated, weak, and unable to eat. She spent three to four days each month in bed. Her husband, who was ordinarily very domi- neering, became at that time the person who waited on her. She continually reminded him of how much she was suffer- ing, and she would contrast her present state of ill health with her good health before marriage. The inference was that her menstrual difficulties were caused by her married sexual life. At least for those few days, Mrs. T. managed to make her husband feel guilty and anxious. What she was doing was attempting to express her hostility toward her husband and all men for putting women in a secondary position. She resented her role as wife and mother, and thought that she would have had a successful career had she not married. Her menstrual disorders were a form of revenge against her husband and the entire male population. It was a way of saying "See what you've done to me and what harm you've caused me."

Penis envy, which frequently shows up in early childhood as children first become aware of the physical differences in male and female bodies, may be resolved at that time, only to surface again during adolescence. Just as a female child may be shocked to see the physical difference between herself and her brother, the female adolescent may suffer an emotional shock when she begins to menstruate. The difference between the sexes is now even more graphically apparent. Feelings of anxiety as well as fantasies of penis loss may surface. There may develop a tendency to attempt to deny menstruation and womanhood and to fantasize that this has happened because of something she has done or her parents have done to her.

One woman patient said, "As an adolescent I had recollections of being in the hospital for an operation when I was a child, and I developed this fantasy that it was through some surgical accident that my penis had been removed. Therefore, menstruation became for me a kind of delayed bleeding of an unhealed wound. I knew the true facts about menstruation, but my daydreams gave me a kind of comfort. Because I associated the bleeding with an operation, I was frequently physically ill during my periods."

Another patient reported, "My father had always wanted a son, and until I began to menstruate, he treated me like a boy. I wanted very much to be like him, and it was a traumatic experience when he no longer treated me the same. I felt that if only I could somehow grow a penis, that would stop my monthly periods, and I would once again be my father's favorite pal. He said I was growing up to be a woman, and I resented it. I resented menstruation because of what it meant in terms of our relationship." This woman became very depressed immediately preceding and during her periods. On one occasion, she had made an unsuccessful attempt at suicide.

A number of patients admit that they had mistaken the first signs of menstruation as punishment for masturbation. They report having been terrified by the first signs of blood and feeling sure that they had contracted some fatal disease.

Since many mothers seem unable to convey an appropriate emotional acceptance of menstruation, it is important that schools or some other adult authority be prepared to perform this function. It is most desirable, of course, that a mother be able to instill in her daughter a pride in womanhood. Instead, too many mothers give their daughters a legacy of confusion, shame, and pain.

Bleeding Does Not Have to Mean Hurting

In our culture, bleeding is associated with hurt and pain. Extending this concept to menstruation causes menstruation to be emotionally identified with injury. If you have some kind of pain in conjunction with your menstrual periods, you may be suffering from a kind of emotional whiplash. Naturally, there can be, and there are, organic causes for menstrual disorders, just as for all forms of illness and disease, but there are also psychosomatic causes which you can change.

Ask yourself if you enjoy suffering each month, or if you would prefer to be able to have a monthly period without feeling sick, tense, or upset by pain. You may find that unconsciously you use your menstrual periods as excuses for poor behavior, for temper flareups, for not getting things done. Your menstrual disorder may be a screen behind which you are hiding your feelings of inadequacy.

If you have a strong sense of masculine identification

and a corresponding dislike of the feminine role, and distrust of yourself as a woman, you may express that through some form of menstrual disorder.

There are a number of menstrual disorders, and most of them can be traced to hidden emotional causes. Premenstrual tension, profuse bleeding (menorrhagia), painful menstruation (dysmenorrhea), scanty menstruation (oligomenorrhea), or the absence of menstrual flow (amenorrhea) can all be caused by guilt, anxieties, resentments, depression, and other forms of tension. Medication offers only temporary help. Taking a pill may relieve the symptom, but it does not treat its real source.

As a woman you have to accept the fact of your femininity, your womanhood, without being resentful. Women are not second-class citizens, and menstruation, instead of being thought of as something unpleasant or painful, should be considered a part of the special quality of being a woman.

There is no reason to be sick, depressed, or unable to perform normal activities during your menstrual periods. If you are unable to function effectively during that time, then you should take a close look at your attitude toward menstruation. Only you can change that attitude, if that is what is responsible for your menstrual problems. Why lose days of activity and enjoyment when it is not necessary? We laugh now at the Victorian woman who was prone to fainting and "sinking" spells, but the twentieth-century woman is in the same class when she lets her menstrual periods dictate what she is going to do and how she is going to feel.

"Doctor, I Feel Like I'm Getting Older Every Hour!"

"Doctor, I feel like I'm getting older every hour!" Mrs. R. said when she came to my office for her first visit. "It seems like everything I see or hear or do reminds me that I'm no longer young. It is making me so nervous that I just don't feel life is worth living!"

It was not surprising to find that Mrs. B.'s symptoms

of anxiety started with menopause. Like many people, she had a misconception of that condition and what it meant. To her, as to millions of other people, the menopause was a dreaded event. Invested with superstition and old wives' tales, menopause has largely been misunderstood.

Like menstruation, menopause is often unnecessarily feared, and this fear is responsible for a variety of psychosomatic ills. Also, like menstruation, menopause is surrounded by an emotional climate of tension and anxiety. We see this in the words or phrases commonly used to describe these two states. Menstruation is often spoken of as "the curse" and sometimes as "falling off the roof," certainly a phrase which implies accident or injury. Menopause is popularly called "the change" or "change of life," which implies a drastic shift in personality, body features, and mental and emotional outlook.

For example, when questioned what she thought about the menopause, Mrs. R. replied, "I know it is a dreadful time, from all I've heard. Things are never the same after a woman starts her change."

Asked more about that "dreadful" time, she explained that women become very nervous, their sexual life ends, their bodies suddenly become old and wrinkled, and in some cases, women's voices change and they grow moustaches or beards. She also said that she had heard that some women are so affected at this time that they become insane and "have to be put away."

It was no wonder that Mrs. R. was upset when she discovered that she was starting the menopause. From all the stories she had heard it would seem that life, especially her emotional and sexual life, had come to a halt. She felt that she was growing old, because she accepted the false premise that menopause means sudden aging.

Mrs. R.'s misgivings about menopause were allayed when she was able to accept the facts about what the menopause is and how it should affect her. "Yes," she was told, "there are body changes, but you can learn to cope with them. And no, you are not ending your emotional or sexual life, nor are you in any danger of losing control over your-self."

In today's world there are medications which can help a woman through this period of physical adjustments during which time her ovaries cease their regular activity, men-struation stops, and there is a change in hormonal balance. Medication can make a woman more comfortable, but it cannot take care of the menopausal problems which are caused by her emotional condition.

The individual woman decides by her attitude whether or not she is going to be able to cope successfully with her menopause. Sometimes, like Mrs. R., she has allowed herself to become conditioned by other people to expect the worst; to expect to be ill or nervous.

Again, mothers and other female relatives have a great deal to do with establishing the attitude about menopause. Mrs. R., for example, remembered that her mother had behaved "strangely" during her menopause and later had said to her, "You can't imagine the suffering I went through!"

It has been observed that women who have had difficul-ties with menstruation also have difficulties with menopause. Although they express relief at no longer having regular monthly periods, their psychosomatic illnesses become related to the menopause. In fact, in many cases they are worse off, since with the menopause their sicknesses and complaints are constant, whereas during menstruation they allowed themselves some days of good health between peri-ods.

Emotional Origins of Menopausal Symptoms and Disorders

We have already seen how superstition, ignorance, and misinformation can cause women to respond poorly during menopause, but there are other emotional causes of menopausal distress.

The woman who thinks of herself solely in terms of motherhood is going to uffer a traumatic shock when she realizes that her days of possible childbearing are ended, and that to some extent her usefulness as a mother is also ended or at least changed. At the time when most women enter menopause their children are themselves mature individuals who have left home and are independently situated.

This loss of maternal responsibility, along with the loss of the reproductive facility, makes many women depressed. Having failed to prepare themselves for this day, they feel suddenly useless.

As one patient remarked with some bitterness, "These are my worthless, declining years." To her, life was only important in relation to her children and their material needs. When she no longer had a family for whom she had to cook, sew, and keep house, she felt of no use. When she no longer could share her children's daily lives, she felt worthless and cast aside. Like so many women, she had not developed her mature personality. During menopause she became depressed, and complained about many minor health conditions. Her reaction was similar to that of an actress who has been playing a lead role for a long time and is suddenly informed that the play closes that night. She had been known as "Mother" for so long that she had remained at a stationary level of personality development and interest. Now that she could no longer play the part of Mother, she was faced with an unemployed stranger—herself.

Naturally, if a woman's self-esteem is based exclusively on her reproductive capacity, she is going to feel let down when she loses that capacity. She has to appreciate herself in some other role. Consequently, for many women, menopause must be a time of re-education in which they take a second look at themselves and their lives. To get over that worthless feeling, they need to think of themselves as personable individuals instead of as cliché figures.

The emotional problems that occur during the menopause are not really new to the woman who suffers from them. Those problems of life adjustment and personality structure have been there for a long time, but they may have been shunted aside while family matters took precedence.

If you have emotional or physical discomforts and illnesses associated with your menopause, it may be because you have too low a level of self-esteem and not enough narcissism, or self-love. While a person may have too much narcissism, it is important to have a healthy amount of it, for self-love is the first step in being able to relate to other people and to the world in general. When you don't love yourself, you begin to have bad emotional reactions, particularly in times of stress or tension. Menopause can be one of those stress periods in which, if you do not have enough self-love, you are going to become engulfed in a variety of psychosomatic illnesses.

You can prevent this breakdown by developing a positive feeling about yourself and what you are capable of doing. If you have neglected other aspects of your personality by concentrating exclusively on your role as a mother, it is not too late to revive other talents and skills or to develop new ones.

Mrs. E. was being treated by her family physician for menopausal symptoms of discomfort, but she still complained of being dizzy, nauseated, and nervous. It was obvious that her problems were psychosomatic in origin.

Not only had Mrs. E. been conditioned by friends to expect to feel ill during menopause, but she now found herself without any interests. Her husband was busy with his work, her two children were married and living in other cities, and she had lost touch with many of her friends and relatives.

Most of her time was spent either watching television, or as she called it, "resting." She neglected her appearance, for she felt that there was nothing to get dressed up for anymore. The impression she gave was of depression and apathy.

During treatment, Mrs. E. showed that she had no real conception of herself as an individual. Because her interest in her family had been so all-consuming, she had neglected her own intellectual development. She felt and acted like a worthless person.

With guidance, she was encouraged to take the first

steps toward rediscovering herself. She joined an adult book-discussion group. She returned to working actively in her church, and she resumed an earlier hobby of weaving, which she had put aside after the birth of her children. It was not long before Mrs. E. was going to the beauty parlor and buying clothes to go with her new life. And as her self-esteem rose in proportion to her sense of personal worth, her previous psychosomatic symptoms diminished to a negligible level.

The Positive Side of Menopause

The reason there are so many psychosomatic problems associated with menopause is that too few women will look at the positive side of the menopause.

Menopause, which is also known as climacteric, can actually be a wonderful time of life. You can make it be some of your best years! It is a period when you have more time for yourself. Instead of feeling sorry for yourself because you don't have so many family responsibilities, take advantage of the fact that at last you have some free time to devote to doing things you want to do. Now you can spend time on hobbies, belong to clubs, do volunteer work or church work, or travel without being tied to the schedule imposed by the demands of your children. You don't have to feel guilty for doing what you want to do.

These special years also give you a chance to have an emotionally healthy, physically satisfying relationship with your husband. Menopause does not mean the end to sex or sexual desire. It can mean a new sense of freedom and enjoyment in your sexual relationship. It is only fair to state, however, that a couple who have had difficulty in sexual relations in premenopausal years will continue to have an unsatisfactory sexual life unless they make some effort to obtain professional counseling and help.

Coinciding with the middle years, menopause affords an opportunity for a second chance at life. A woman does not have to be a slave to psychosomatic symptoms related to menopause any more than she has to suffer because of her menstrual periods. The menopause years can be years of ripened maturity which add dimensions to the personality.

Thinking of menopause as the end of reproductive fertility is correct, but there is no end to mental or creative fertility.

The Male Menopause, or the Forty-Year Syndrome

Although men do not go through the same obvious physical changes as women do during the menopause, there is a male climacteric. A man, like a woman, may become irritable, nervous, complain of not feeling well, and secretly worry about diminishing sexual ability. He may also worry about getting old, and at that time start to baby himself during periods of minor illnesses.

And as with women, men will have as much trouble and sickness during this period as they expect to have! The man who worries about his sexual potency will find that the worry itself has an adverse affect upon his ability to have satisfactory sexual relations.

It is just as ridiculous for a man in his middle years to decide that his life is over as it is for a woman to equate the cessation of menstruation with old age and uselessness as an individual.

Yes, there are physiological changes and biological differences as a man grows older, but the importance is not in his chronological age but in his conception of himself. I have known men in their seventies and eighties who were intellectually alert, sexually vigorous, and free of any kind of psychosomatic complaints. These were men who enjoyed their middle and late years as much as any part of their lives.

The middle-aged man who complains of male menopausal symptoms is a man who has always had problems in adjustment and personality. What he does after age forty is to use his age as an excuse for his own shortcomings and failures. A man does not suddenly suffer a nervous breakdown or become a failure because of his age. The potential for some kind of disability was already there; all he has done is to take advantage of a certain time in his life.

Anxiety and apprehension about the future cause most of the symptoms in male climacteric. Again as with women, the men who have high levels of self-esteem, who have self-pride and outside interests, are not going to fall victims to the biological changes imposed by nature.

How to Restore Emotional and Physical Potency

You can restore emotional and physical vigor to your life without taking patent medicines or special cures. In the majority of cases, the psychological and emotional outlook determines the state of one's health.

One way to restore that vigor in your life is to keep your appearance up. If you look in the mirror and see a fat, bald-headed man or a fat woman with sagging shoulders and breasts, naturally you are going to become depressed. You will literally make yourself sick by accepting this image of a tired, worn-out person.

Straighten up your posture, spruce up your appearance, and when necessary, lose those extra pounds. Slouching is a discouraging habit. Carrying around unnecessary weight will make you tired. These things can make you feel old and ugly.

If gray hair bothers you, dye it to a more youthful color. If baldness makes you feel prematurely old, wear a hairpiece. But start with the inner you, for no amount of external aids can automatically give you the feeling of potency that you desire. Those other things can aid you, but by themselves they can't accomplish the miracle you want.

Keeping busy is the best way to stay alert and vigorous. Your mental keenness will be reflected in your physical good health. A mature approach to your menopause years can work magic in your life. I have observed that the people who are not bothered by "change of life" are those people who are actively living their lives. You can do the same!

XI

The Psychosomatic Basis
of Accidents

How "Accidental" Are Accidents?

We all know what an accident is—by definition, at least. According to the dictionary, an accident is "any event that happens unexpectedly, without a deliberate plan or cause." But just how accidental are most accidents? If we are to look at accidents from the psychological point of view, that definition would have to be altered to read, "without a *consciously* deliberate plan or cause."

As psychosomatic responses to life, accidents come from our unconscious. They are another way of expressing various emotions through body reactions, just as are headaches, backaches, diarrhea, heartburn, and the many other ills we have been talking about. If anything, accidents are a more dramatic form of psychosomatic response. For that reason, frequently they are also more unconsciously satisfying to the person who is involved.

In 1970 in the United States there were 10,900,000 injuries from accidents. The cost of those accidents in terms of lost wages, medical expenses, and insurance costs was over sixteen billion dollars.

Were you a part of that statistical picture? All of us tend to forget that the accident or illness we have is only a small part of the total picture. When viewed as a whole, the expense and time-loss from accidents in this country is disastrous. And it is shameful, because a major portion of those accidents could have been avoided.

Admittedly, it is difficult to determine exactly what proportion of accidents are psychosomatic in origin, but we do know that the proportion is shockingly high.

"Carelessness" is the reason frequently given as the cause of an accident. However, carelessness is the result of something else, and it is that something else that we have to investigate in determining the causes of accidents.

Some Psychosomatic Causes of Accidents

In almost every accident there are two causes. One is the actual or easily seen cause, such as when a driver swerves his car and runs into a tree. The other is the hidden cause, and that is the real reason for the accident. In our example of the car colliding with a tree, the hidden cause is what made the driver swerve the car in the first place. Was he not paying attention to his driving because of some strong emotion he was feeling? In many cases it is found that the driver involved in an accident had been in a tense personal situation just prior to the accident. His mind was not on his driving because he was feeling sad, guilty, depressed, or angry. His conscious mind was driving the car, but his unconscious was forcing him to drive in such a way that an accident was almost inevitable.

I talked to a driver who was involved in a one-car accident very similar to the one I have been using as an illustration. He admitted that just prior to the accident his thoughts were angry.

"I had a quarrel with my wife over money matters," he explained. "She had been upset for over a week because I had bought a new car instead of putting the money in a savings account as she thought I should. I felt that since the money was a bonus for some special work I had done, it was up to me to decide what to do with it. On the day we argued I walked out of the house and jumped into the car and drove off at a high speed. The accident happened less than two miles from the house on a road I had traveled every day for the last twelve years! What do you think happened to me, Doctor? I've never done anything like that before."

It was not difficult to explain to him what had happened. He had satisfied some ego desires by spending the bonus money as he wanted and by getting something big and flashy in exchange for his hours of work. However, his superego, the repository of his moral judgments, was not satisfied with his choice and let him know by making him feel guilty. His superego set up a demand that he be punished for gratifying his personal wishes instead of paying attention to what his conscience told him to do.

In addition, his sense of guilt intensified when he became angry with his wife, since unconsciously he knew he was treating her badly in order to justify his own actions. As a result, his unconscious set up an accident-prone situation, and he responded by wrecking his car. Two things were satisfied by the accident; he was punished by being physically hurt, and he was deprived of his new car.

It must be pointed out, however, that had this patient's moral judgments been different, he might not have had such an accident, as he would not have felt guilty about buying the car in the face of his wife's disapproval.

Each individual's unconscious sets up a very personal response to any given situation. That is why some people have psychosomatic illnesses and accidents, while others go through life unhampered or unaffected by things that happen to them. It is not unusual to hear someone say, "Well, if that had happened to me, I would be sick about it!" And they probably *would* be sick—or have an accident.

Psychosomatic accidents are caused by the same conditions that cause psychosomatic illnesses. Some of the most common causes are anger, anxiety, depression, guilt, fear, and worry.

One man who was worried about his financial affairs slipped and fell down a flight of stairs. His accident was an expression of his unconscious desire to be freed from any blame in connection with his money problems. Certainly, when he was in the hospital no one was going to reproach him for mismanaging his finances. At the same time that his unconscious was giving him a way out of his money problems at least temporarily, it was also punishing him for his failure. He was in physical pain; he was suffering discomfort.

Self-Punishment Motivations and Accidents

Many people do not want to accept this idea of self-punishment as a determining factor in accidents. To them the whole concept of an accident is that it is an unavoidable circumstance, almost in the primitive sense that it comes from some outside force or fate. I have had people ask, "Why would I want to hurt myself?" Yet, to hurt themselves is precisely what their unconscious is demanding from them.

Self-punishment is a natural result of a strong moral code. And for centuries in this country we have been conditioned to accept the premise that one has to be punished in some way for any misdeed. This belief has persisted despite some very obvious changes in the general moral code. The greater permissiveness of today's society has not altogether permeated the personal moral structure. Therefore, among many people their own misdeeds still arouse sufficient guilt to result in a need for punishment. When punishment is not forthcoming from outside sources, the only way to expiate the guilt is in self-punishment.

Accidents are one of the most effective ways to satisfy what one feels as a need for self-punishment, for they almost always guarantee some measure of inconvenience and pain. In some cases the effects of an accident are so long-lasting that a person is punished for the rest of his life.

There is a correlation between the severity of the accident and the degree of guilt. Ben E. frequently used accidents as a self-punishment device. The kind of accident he had was directly related to how guilty and upset he was over some specific incident. For example, when he took some stamps and stationery from the office where he worked, he felt guilty because he knew it was a form of stealing. That same evening he tripped over a footstool and bruised his ankle. Another time, after lying to his wife about his activities during a company convention, Ben shut the car door on his hand and smashed three of his fingers.

There are impulses in your unconscious which propel you inexorably toward self-punishment acts. However, if you can determine the relationship between your accidents and your feelings of guilt, you can learn to control your tendency to hurt yourself physically.

When you feel guilty over something, you have a high potential for accident or illness, depending upon what form

of psychosomatic reaction you use to express your unconscious feelings of emotional distress and guilt. If you can
learn to recognize these danger times, you can learn to control your tendency to punish yourself with an accident.
Guilt should be dealt with on a level more rational than re-
sorting to having accidents.

Examine your feelings of guilt to see if their degree is
commensurate with the supposed offense you have commit-
ted. Too many people have feelings of guilt that are far out
of proportion. However, if your feeling of guilt is reasonable
for what you have done, it is better to look for ways to
amend the situation or make some kind of restitution instead of punishing yourself with an accident.

Although guilt is the main cause of self-punishing accidents, it is not the only one. Feelings of anger may start the
pattern of self-punishment, for anger is frequently accompanied by guilt feelings, and the two combine to cause psychosomatic reactions.

As I mentioned earlier, many automobile accidents involve drivers who are driving while under the influence of
anger. This means that they have a high potential for com-
mitting some kind of self-destructive act.

Although there are other causes of psychosomatic accidents, the victim should consider what part the voice of his
conscience played in making him do the careless or foolish
thing that caused the accident.

Have You Had Your Accident Today?

There is an old and rather timeworn joke which has a
man meeting a friend who is hobbling along on crutches.
"Hello," the man calls out solicitously. "Have an accident?"
To which his friend replies, "No, thanks, I've just had
one."

Old as the joke is, it illustrates a point about the accident-prone personality—he has accepted accidents as a part
of his way of life. He may put the blame on "bad luck" or
admit to a certain amount of clumsiness or carelessness, but

whatever reason he puts forth, he does expect to have accidents happen to him. His expectations are rarely diasppointed, and his whole life may be highlighted by accidents.

At a party I heard a woman whose entire memory system seemed to be connected to her accident-prone personality. She used such sentences as, "Yes, that was the summer I broke my leg," "It was the year I was burned by the pot of hot soup," and "We had a blue Pontiac then; I remember because I ran into a lamppost with it."

The woman I have just quoted probably would have denied that she was accident-prone. Most people do not see themselves as willing victims but rather as individuals singled out by some unkind fate. How do we determine who should be labeled accident-prone? How do you know if you are accident-prone?

The accident-prone personality has certain emotional characteristics, as well as specific behavior patterns. Anyone who has a series of accidents can be considered accident-prone. He or she is probably emotionally immature and may have difficulty in coping with the stresses and tensions of everyday circumstances.

The accident-prone person has low self-esteem. He does not take proper care of himself because he does not have enough interest in his own survival. Just as you tend to be careless with objects you consider to be of little worth, so can you treat yourself in the same way. If you think that you have little value as a person, you will have psychosomatic accidents which reveal this lack of personal interest and concern.

Robert Z. called himself "unlucky," his wife called him "careless," while his friends simply shook their heads and wondered what would happen next to Robert. In one year he had a sprained ankle, a broken rib, a black eye, and badly burnt hands. All of the accidents were caused by what Robert called "unavoidable circumstances"—an automobile accident, an open door in a dark room, a box left on the cellar stairs, a box of matches that suddenly burst into flames when Robert was trying to light logs in his fireplace.

Analysis revealed that the unconscious motivation for Robert's accident-prone pattern came from disgust with himself because he felt that he hadn't succeeded in life.

He felt that he had let himself down. He admitted that each accident had been preceded by some episode which he considered to be disappointing or embarrassing. On one occasion he felt that he had appeared inadequate at a company dinner by not being able to handle certain social graces. On another occasion he felt that he had acted like a fool at a dinner party because, although he had known a great deal about the subjects being discussed, he had failed to speak up. His automobile accident had occurred right after he had been passed over for a promotion.

The gap between Robert's performance and what he felt he should have done was so painful to him that his instinctive reaction was one of disgust—disgust directed at himself. On one visit he remarked, "I'm just worthless. I shouldn't even be taking up your time, Doctor." He frequently made other self-deprecating remarks. Robert's accidents were a way of responding to his feelings of personal inadequacy.

When he learned to raise his self-esteem and to value himself as a person, Robert lost his feelings of disgust and inferiority. And the accidents that had plagued his life stopped happening.

The accident-prone person is sometimes seriously emotionally ill. He may be using accidents as an expression of his unconscious wish for death. This death wish can be prompted by anger, guilt, or low self-esteem. Accident-prone people flirt with death because they unconsciously consider it the only possible solution to their problems.

But having accidents is a safe substitute for suicide; safe in the sense that the individual is not blamed, nor does he usually lose his life. He can go to the brink but not take that final, irrevocable step.

A serious accident allows a person to be removed from the scene of his troubles without being castigated for it. One man who did not get along with his foreman at work but could not afford to give up his job became totally disabled in an industrial accident. The accident made it possible for him to stop his work, and since no one could precisely fix the blame for what had happened, he received sympathy as well as praise for his stoic response to his disability without being blamed for being careless. And, although he had not consciously caused the accident, his unconscious desire for a way out of his work-related problem had made it possible for him to become an accident victim.

Everyone should be alert to his own remarks and those of others that may indicate an accident-producing situation. Such comments as "This job is killing me," and "I would rather be dead than . . ." indicate a danger point at which time accidents can happen.

Some people are generally accident-prone, others have accident-prone periods. These periods are related to stress situations.

Mr. O., an intelligent man in his mid-fifties, came for counseling because of a rash of accidents that had happened to him in the past few months. Although the accidents were all minor in nature, he was concerned, for he felt that he was in some way responsible for this change in his behavior pattern.

Mr. O. denied being worried about anything. His business affairs were going well, his marriage was happy, and he had an active and satisfying social and civic life. Nevertheless, it was apparent that these frequent accidents were an expression of some unconscious tension or emotion.

During his analysis it was brought out that he had gone through a similar accident-prone period earlier in his life, during adolescence.

"That was a terrible time," he remarked. "I had some automobile accidents. I fell out of a tree while picking some fruit. I broke an arm ice-skating and sprained an ankle playing baseball. It was one thing after another. My family was always taking me to the doctor."

Asked about his feelings during this period, he at first characterized them as "just the usual interest in sports, cars, and girls." But digging more deeply into his memories of that period, he was able to bring out some that were repressed. Many of those memories were connected with his adolescent sexual fears and fantasies.

"I was small for my age," he said, "and did not mature as rapidly as the other boys I knew. My slow physical sexual development bothered me, but I didn't know what I could do about it. I used to wish that I could ask someone about it, but I didn't feel that I could talk to my parents about sexual matters. I had fears that I would never develop sexually and that I was some kind of a freak! Then suddenly one year everything changed, and I just caught up with the other boys and there were no more problems."

"Were there any more accidents?"

"No. I remember that my parents said that at last I had gotten coordinated enough to stop getting hurt."

Mr. O. had had accidents during his adolescence primarily because he had felt sexually inferior. His accidents had had a secondary purpose too, for they had caused him to be taken to the doctor's office where, he unconsciously hoped, his poor sexual development would be treated.

Now in his middle years, Mr. O. was repeating adolescent patterns of behavior. Asked if he presently had any sexual anxieties, he at first said he had none. But later he admitted that he did fear becoming sexually impotent.

That had happened to a friend, who blamed it on his age, and Mr. O. reasoned that if it could happen to his friend, it could happen to him. He hesitated to seek medical advice on such a theoretical problem, so he unconsciously found another way to get a doctor's attention.

Once we had discussed his sexual anxieties and the question of sexual impotence, Mr. O.'s accident-proneness vanished along with his fears.

Any type of stress situation or general atmosphere of worry and tension in your life can bring about a period of accidents. As with psychosomatic illnesses, you have to find and treat the underlying cause rather than deal only with the immediate problem. Accidents are another form of symptom that indicates trouble somewhere beneath the surface.

"Look, I'm Bleeding!"

Have you ever been in a group when one person suddenly gets the attention of everyone else by injuring himself? He may cut a finger, trip and fall, spill something on himself, or choke on something he's eating. Whatever the accident, it is usually used by the victim to focus attention on himself.

The immature person, like a child, wishes to be the center of attention, and he may discover that having accidents is one way to insure getting attention from others.

Of course, everybody has periods in which he would like to be the focal point of people's interest. This behavior is not unusual or abnormal, but most people know how to control this impulse and keep it within acceptable limits. Therefore, they try to get attention by some kind of achievement or special excellence, rather than by accidents.

The individual who does not have a strong sense of personal achievement has to look for recognition in some other way. Having an accident means instant attention, not only from family and friends, but even from strangers who may be present. Having an accident means getting sympathy and special consideration. Accidents can keep a person from being anonymous. Unfortunately, they do not guarantee continued concern from others, for people soon tire of the accident-prone person.

At a party, I saw a woman sitting alone who suddenly commanded the attention of the entire group by spilling hot coffee on her hand. It was an accident, but it was also a sure-fire device to get attention. From the time the accident occurred until the party was over, that woman was never alone. She was the center of sympathetic attention. Judging by the look on her face, she enjoyed her position, despite the pain of her burn.

We have all seen a child fall down, get up and run to

his mother, and then burst into tears. We smile at the obvious bid for sympathy and attention, but this is precisely what the accident-prone adult does. He too runs to others, in a literal or figurative sense, and cries for sympathy.

Behind this appeal for sympathy is, of course, a cry for love. The accident-prone person, like the child, needs reassurance from others. The child goes to his mother, father, or teacher, while the adult has to go to other adults.

Closely connected with this idea of being injured in order to get attention is the wish to have operations. To a seriously ill person in the hospital, it seems preposterous that there are people on the outside who long to be hospitalized. But there are people who demand unnecessary operations. They are sure that they need the operation even when it is contraindicated by competent medical opinion, so they usually go from one doctor to another, seeking one who will perform the surgery. Such people often appear to have symptoms that would require an operation. They are not consciously faking these symptoms. Their unconscious has taken over and made it easy for them to appear in need of surgery.

To the accident-prone person, there are some advantages in surgery and hospitalization. Certainly, surgery is the ultimate in being able to say, "Look, I'm bleeding!" In Chapter 4 we discussed secondary gain, an advantage to be gained from an illness. Operations provide many secondary gains.

The patient who has an operation immediately becomes the center of attention to a number of people. He feels enveloped in a circle of concern. And this circle includes not only family, friends, and acquaintances, but doctors, nurses, and other hospital personnel as well. To the person who feels unhappy or unappreciated, this secondary gain in itself makes the operation worth while.

There are other secondary gains, one of which is the amount of "mothering" received by the patient. Hospitalization is a period of enforced regression. The adult once more becomes a child, or when seriously ill, a baby. He no longer has any obligation to carry out his adult responsibilities. He does not even have to care for his physical needs if he is incapable of doing so or thinks that he is too sick to do so. Other people will feed him, bathe him, change his bed linen and pajamas, and bring him a bedpan. He can be in an absolutely regressive state of infantilism and not feel guilty about it. Nor does he have to show any interest in outside affairs, either his own, those of others, or of the world in general. He can be a completely self-centered person without being blamed for it. No wonder that people with emotional problems often turn to some form of psychosomatic illness or accident to get the love and attention they need.

How to Defeat that Unconscious Desire to Hurt Yourself

You do not need to have an accident-prone personality. You can learn to defeat that unconscious desire to hurt yourself. If you feel that accidents play too large a part in your life, or if you suspect that you are using operations to compensate for unfulfilled emotional needs, you should dig beneath the surface and look for your true motivations.

When your superego demands self-punishment, shout back at it, "Why should I be punished?" Study the facts in your own case. Perhaps your demands for punishment are out of proportion to what you have done. Help yourself become aware of other ways of rectifying or atoning for what you have done.

You may also have to change some of your notions of morality if they have been imposed upon you. For example, one man who had been raised to believe that card-playing was sinful had an automobile accident on his way home from a poker game in which he had won some money. He admitted that at the time of the accident he was thinking of what his father would have said about his winnings. He was sill unconsciously under the moral influence of his parents, and therefore he felt guilty. Yet, as a middle-aged man living in a society different from that of his parents, he should have been able to accept what was good and useful in their standards and discard or amend the rest.

The accident-prone person is frequently one who is unable to adapt to changing conditions. You should ask yourself what part your inability to compromise plays in your accidents.

Accidents are basically antisocial acts. You are demonstrating a contempt for yourself and others by your carelessness. Accidents mean inconvenience both for yourself and for those who are involved with you. Why do you want to make a nuisance of yourself? You will have to determine whether you behave in this way because you want attention, love, and concern from others. But you will also have to face the fact that this is not an adult way to get any of the things you want. Look for other ways in which you can openly and honestly earn the attention and respect of people.

If you develop some respect and esteem for yourself, you will take better care of your body. You won't be tempted or unconsciously driven to behave in a way that leads to accidents. You won't unconsciously envy people in the hospital, because you will have more going for you on the outside.

In a very simplified way we can put it like this: you can make your life or break your bones—the choice is yours.

XII

"I'd Rather Die Than Grow Old"

Death and Aging: Twin Fears

Death and aging remain the most traumatic events in people's lives. Yet these two inescapable events need not arouse the anxiety they do. Fears of aging and death are responsible for many psychosomatic illnesses. Your attitude toward these aspects of life determines much of your personal happiness and adjustment. An inability to accept aging and dying as a part of living may not only make you miserable, but may seriously affect your productive years.

Some people are so terrified by death that in a very real sense it kills them. They literally talk themselves into it. Others are more afraid of aging and come to the illogical and unhealthy conclusion: "I'd rather die than grow old." And far too many people equate aging with dying, so they suffer doubly as they see the months and years pass by.

The problems that accompany aging are more than physical; for many people they are primarily psychological. It is a matter of attitude.

Death is a part of the total life process. The person who has not been able to fully face his own aging and eventual death cannot really be said to have lived completely.

You have to learn to face and conquer these twin fears—fear of death and fear of aging. Being able to understand their place in your life and being able to cope with them means an enriched life for yourself and a freedom from the unnecessary psychosomatic ills related to these two fears.

"Help! I'm Getting All Wrinkled!"

We must distinguish between aging physically and aging psychologically. Aging as a psychological process can begin at any age, or it can never occur. Physical aging is not only inevitable, it is irreversible; psychological aging can be stopped at any time, and reversed.

Growing old is a universal phenomenon, but you are

apt to notice aging in others more quickly than in yourself. Then that fateful day arrives when you stop to take a good look in the mirror and you see an image which does not correspond to your mental image of yourself. You might exclaim aloud or mentally something like, "Help! I'm getting all wrinkled!"

Yes, it is a shock, but it need not send you off on a bout of self-pity or a fruitless expedition in search of the Fountain of Youth.

The problem that most people have upon seeing this new image of themselves is that they immediately change their mental attitudes to correspond with their concepts of age. It is very similar to an attitude depicted a few years ago in a popular magazine cartoon. An older couple is shown walking briskly out to the mailbox where they draw out an envelope containing their first social security check. As the realization of their retirement comes to them, they slump, and are shown helping each other slowly back to the house.

This concept of aging as a necessarily deteriorating process has come down to us from the past and is no longer valid in the late twentieth century. Seventy-five years ago the average life-expectancy in the United States was fifty years or less. Today it is more like seventy years. A number of things have made this longer life-expectancy possible. The advance of medical science is one, but less rigorous living and working conditions are also responsible. We know more about nutrition, and we eat better. We live in more healthful surroundings. But, most important, we know we don't have to get old in the sense of looking and acting like an "old" person.

Seventy-five years ago older men and women were expected to dress soberly, usually in black or other subdued colors. It was almost as if they were in mourning for their past years. Older people were also expected to severely limit their activities. And since the life span was shorter in those days than it is now, old age was thought to occur at a much earlier chronological age.

Unfortunately, many people still believe that aging means the end of active life. Too many people use their later years as a time to "enjoy" poor health, to abstain from the sensual pleasures, and wait for death.

It is true that your hearing may become less acute, your eyesight may be less sharp, and some of your motor reactions less quick. But you can develop compensatory skills, with and without mechanical aids. A good hearing-aid, adequate glasses, a cane if necessary, false teeth, and other devices will help you feel less old. And if that gray or white hair bothers you, dye it. Women who are bothered by wrinkles can learn to apply makeup skillfully so that the appearance of age, while not concealed, is less noticeable. Both men and women can learn to dress in a way that de-emphasizes their lack of youthful figure, if they feel it is necessary.

There is no substitution, however, for your mental attitude toward aging. You can dye your hair, you can dress in younger styles, but if you feel old, you are going to look and act old!

When you see that first sign of what you consider age—whether it is gray hairs, wrinkles, or a stooping posture—you are going to have to decide whether or not you want to dwell on this aging process or stay youthful (or to use a word that I think is preferable—"ageless").

The ageless person enjoys life every day and in many ways. He does not circumscribe his life with an artificial barrier of years. He does not limit his scope of interests or his activities according to the calendar. He usually forgets his actual age, because in a very real sense, he has *no* age.

Many young people are very conscious of being young, and many old people are very conscious of being old. Both groups talk about life in terms of their ages. Both groups tend to focus on age as the center of concern for themselves and others. There are others who think both groups very boring.

If you are in the chronological age bracket that is com-

monly thought of as old, listen to your conversation and to
your own thoughts. How many times a day do you make
some kind of reference to your age? How many times a day
do you use your age as an excuse for either not doing something or for some personality peculiarity?

This was the attitude of Mrs. B., who was only sixty-
five years old but looked more like seventy-five or eighty.
She walked slowly, shoulders bent. Her clothes were dowdy,
her hair done in an unbecoming style. She ate only certain
foods, claiming that because of her age it was difficult for
her to digest many things. In addition, she complained of
suffering from insomnia, but always added that the reason
must be that "old" people don't sleep so much.

Talking with Mrs. B. was a chore because she was so
concerned with her own problems, which she related to
what she called "my advanced years."

Mrs. B. explained that old age had come to her when
her husband had died a year after she retired from her
teaching position. A widow and no longer working, at age
sixty-two, Mrs. B. sank into a kind of emotional lethargy
that was rapidly rendering her inactive. She admitted that
her concept of age was based on stories her mother and
grandmother had told her. She expected to be old just because she had reached a certain chronological age and because she was a widow and no longer working. Because she
was an intelligent woman, she was able, with help, to see
the fallacy of her reasoning. She was not living in the time
of her mother or grandmother. She still had many useful,
productive years.

A year after treatment, you would not have recognized
Mrs. B., and in fact, many of her acquaintances had trouble
getting used to her new appearance and attitude. She still
didn't look her age—she looked and acted at least ten years
younger! She had discovered that age was mental rather
than chronological. She had changed her style of clothes
and hair and was busy doing volunteer work with a group
of underprivileged children. She no longer had time to feel
sorry for herself as an "old person." Her quick steps, glow

ing face, and smiling eyes told you that here was a person who was truly ageless and a useful member of society.

Sex and Aging

Many mistaken and controversial ideas are associated with sex and aging. Generally, however, doctors and other experts agree that there is no reason to assume that sexual interest and drive diminish solely because of age. Nor is there any reason to believe that sexual activity is bad for older people.

The basic problem that older people have with sex is one that is inherent in our society. There is an assumption that sexual activity should diminish or cease after a certain age. This assumption is made upon moral grounds rather than any scientific fact. In some people's view sex is still tinged with guilt feelings.

We learned in Chapter 9 that sexual impotence can occur when a man has low self-esteem or a feeling of loss of personal identity and worth. As a man gets older, he may have some doubts about his usefulness and his own physical state. If he allows those doubts to take over his thinking, he will suffer from impotence as well as other psychosomatic ailments related to his attitude about aging. A woman may suffer from sexual frigidity for the same reasons.

Both men and women can and do remain sexually interested and active well into their seventies and eighties and beyond, if their general physical and mental health are good. The capacity for sexual enjoyment has no connection with chronological age.

The individual who willingly gives up sexual activity upon reaching what he considers the "proper" age to become old is usually one who did not get much enjoyment out of sex even when young. The woman who has always disliked and dreaded sexual intercourse uses her menopausal symptoms and older years as an excuse for no longer engaging in sexual activities. The man who had sexual adjustment problems when he was younger is glad to use his age as a reason for avoiding sex.

Sexual organs don't atrophy, but an individual's psyche may, to the extent that he refuses to live a normal sex life. Sexual activity can continue as long as one wishes it to. To stop arbitrarily at a certain age is as unnecessary as to stop eating good food after age fifty or sixty. It is true that not eating food would result in death, but not to enjoy sex and its related interpersonal communication pleasures can result in a kind of death of the personality.

Becoming Old Is a Personal Decision

The facts of physical aging are not to be denied, but they need not make you old. You have to be willing to accept the physical aging process while maintaining a youthful spirit.

That being old is a matter of personal decision can be seen if you look around at other people. Some are old at twenty; some suddenly age in their forties; others never seem to age.

The fear of aging can wreck your health and peace of mind. It can give you such psychosomatic ailments as chronic indigestion, insomnia, headaches, muscle spasms, and other complaints which, though vague in nature, are a nuisance to you. If you expect age to mean a steady deterioration of your body, you will experience aches and pains. It can become a vicious circle—you refuse to be physically active because of your "aging" condition, and thus you may actually become less agile and less able to do things.

In the country today every tenth person is sixty-five years of age or older. The figures for 1970 showed that at that time there were thirteen thousand people who were more than one hundred years old! And those figures will increase in the years to come.

Why cut yourself out of life long before death? That is what you do when you succumb to the idea that aging is a time of negativism and withdrawal. If you are not in an older age-group now, there is time to rid yourself of the concept of older people as prone to sickness, grouchy and garrulous, living lives of dependency. If you are older, you

can change your self-image so that you do not fit the stereo-
type of the aging person. And you can change your life so
that you are not subject to the psychosomatic ills which are
associated with aging.

There are no magic formulas or chemicals which can
restore youth, but you can experience real rejuvenation by
changing your mental attitude about aging. Don't be afraid
of growing older; if you keep busy and happy, you will
hardly notice the passing of the years.

The Life-Death Relationship

Perhaps the greatest fear in most lives is the fear of
death. This is understandable, since death is an unknowable
phenomenon. Yet it is not possible either to escape or ignore
it.

Death is the final aspect of life. Life and death are inseparable. To attempt to deny the existence of death is to
deny life; it is a negative act. Accepting the concept of death
is not to be confused with a wish for death. It means,
rather, understanding that life is finite, and therefore wishing to live your life fully. It means that you do not want to
postpone doing things, but at all times you will try to
achieve your best and develop all of your capabilities.

People who fear death frequently suffer from psychosomatic illnesses which may be quite severe and even incapacitating. To them, each illness is a prelude to death. A
cut immediately means blood poisoning; a cold, pneumonia;
a headache indicates a brain tumor, and the need for an operation is a sign that funeral arrangements should definitely
be made! This may sound humorous, but it is very serious
and emotionally distressing to the person who feels that
way. In this connection, it seems appropriate to quote these
famous lines from Shakespeare's *Julius Caesar.*

> *Cowards die many times before their deaths;*
> *The valiant never taste of death but once.*
> *Of all the wonders that I yet have heard,*

It seems to me most strange that men should fear;
Seeing that death, a necessary end,
Will come when it will come.

A fear of death can lead people to magnify every minor ache, pain, or physical upset. Such cowardice can cause people to suffer a thousand deaths in their lives. They cannot enjoy living because they are so sure that they are dying.

This was the case with Peter S. He was convinced that he was dying of cancer. Even when his family doctor and a specialist told him that he was well and had no signs of cancer, he refused to accept their conclusions. Behind his insistence that he was dying was a strong fear of death. He so feared it that he constantly looked for and anticipated it. The gastrointestinal trouble he suffered from was psychosomatic in origin and came from his anxious state of mind. He refused to think in terms of curing his trouble, but only in finding someone who would confirm his self-diagnosis.

What is your attitude toward your own death? How many times have you imagined that you had or would soon have some fatal illness? Do you know why you have the attitude toward death that you have? Since we start dying when we are born, we also start knowing about death early in life and forming our emotional attitude about it. Those early experiences and feelings condition our adult responses to death.

Childhood and Adolescent Traumas in Relation to Adult Attitudes Toward Death

If as a child or adolescent you suffered any traumatic shock in relation to death, you have a greater chance of having a problem in your adult attitude toward it. You may develop an unreasonable fear of death.

If you did not properly and realistically understand death as a child, you need to acquire an understanding of it as an adult. Otherwise, you will not be able to cope with it successfully. You will not be able to face the fact of your own death or the deaths of loved ones and friends. Death will continue to be a traumatic experience which will prevent you from living a normal life or from responding in a normal way when the threat of death or death itself touches your life in some fashion. You will suffer an excess of trauma in a death situation.

A lasting fear of death may come from unresolved separation anxiety. We have already discussed separation anxiety in relation to psychosomatic illness. Separation anxiety is always present to some degree, but it can become intensified during a stress period. Death is one of those stress periods. The aged frequently suffer from separation anxiety as they lose family members and friends through death.

One man told me, "I don't know what to do with my father. Each time one of his friends dies, he becomes ill and takes to his bed. At his age, seventy-six, there are quite a few deaths among his acquaintances. I know that he's worrying about his own death. Actually, he is in good health, but these emotional bouts are getting him down."

For a child, the death of a pet, a favorite teacher, playmates, or relatives can produce lasting results. A child may also suffer shock or separation anxiety from the loss of a favorite toy or the unexplained absence of a favorite adult. Divorce, too, is not easily understood by the very young child and may be equated with death.

Mr. W. became very upset whenever a death occurred in his immediate circle of acquaintances; even hearing or reading about the death of a stranger made him depressed. As he became older, Mr. W. became more emotionally upset by death. He began to have morbid fears, fantasies, and dreams about the possible deaths of his family members and himself. He became a perpetual worrier about their health and safety and developed a chronic psychosomatic cough.

Analysis revealed that Mr. W.'s abnormal reactions to death could be traced to a childhood traumatic experience involving the death of a pet.

"I was about seven years old," he recalled, "and my best friend and constant companion was my dog, Skippy, who had been with me since I was a baby. One day when I came home from school, Skippy wasn't there to meet me as usual. My mother said that Skippy had run away. I didn't think that Skippy would leave of his own accord, and I decided someone must have taken him. I went out to look for him, and after a fruitless search, returned home tired and crying. It was by accident that I discovered Skippy's body under our porch, covered by an old blanket. He had been run over by a car. At that moment I hated my mother because she had lied to me. I also learned firsthand about losing something very dear to me."

Mr. W. explained that this had been his first experience with death, and the combination of his pet's dying and the fear of death that his mother's attitude conveyed resulted in a kind of emotional shock. Its effect on his emotional development had not only persisted into adulthood but had become more traumatic as he grew older.

Psychosomatic Illnesses as Responses to Deaths of Loved Ones

Psychosomatic illnesses are common responses to death, especially when the period of mourning is either too short or is not permitted. Often, a survivor will adopt symptoms that are related to the terminal symptoms of the dead person. This is a form of negative identification.

In one case a woman whose mother had been a hypochondriac but who died of natural causes developed the same symptoms her mother had always had. Prior to her mother's death, she had not had any health problems. In another case, a man suffered from severe chest pains after his father died of a heart attack.

Psychosomatic illnesses are sometimes used by the survivor because he feels guilty about being alive when his spouse, best friend, or relative has died. By being ill, he is in effect saying, "Yes, I am still alive, but I'm not really enjoying life because I'm too sick."

The illness of a survivor can be traced to any one of three factors or to an insidious combination of all three. Separation anxiety, faulty or improper use of the mourning period, or intensified fears of one's own death can cause a survivor to fall into a period of emotional and physical decline. It is not unusual to hear a person say, "I have just never felt well since —————— died." Occasionally, an individual will ascribe his sudden ill health to the strain he was under during the illness and subsequent death of a loved one.

In separation anxiety, death is the ultimate experience and produces the most intense anxiety. There are two aspects to this fear of separation by death. One is your fear of losing others through their deaths; the second is your fear of being lost to others and losing your own personality through your own death. Both aspects can produce psychosomatic illnesses.

You can overcome the fear of separation-by-death through the normal process of mourning. It is in this way that we retain certain elements of the lost object of our love. This is primarily a process of identification. You absorb into your life and thinking certain aspects of the dead person, usually retaining the best part of that person's life and thinking. In a sense, you carry on where he left off in his own life.

Identification is a method of incorporation. Because of this process of identification the dead are not really separated from us. This same identification process holds true for your own death. Your survivors will continue to relate to you and will identify with the positive aspects of your life and personality. In addition, therefore, to the satisfaction and happiness derived during life from a healthy, creative personality, there is added the bonus of your continued effect upon the lives of others after you have ceased to live. This may be your chief claim to immortality—the memory of you in the minds of those still living. Thus, there is no need to fear separation by death, because there is never any real psychological separation.

The Proper Emotional Response to Death

The proper emotional response to death is to go into a period of mourning. This is a normal emotional reaction and may prevent the development of psychosomatic illnesses related to the death situation.

The intensity and length of the period of mourning will naturally vary with the individual and will also be related to the importance to you of the person you have lost.

You must learn to accept both the reality of death and the need for mourning. Crying is a part of mourning, as it is an expression of natural grief. Tears should not be bottled up inside, for they are therapeutic. They relieve your immediate feelings of stress and tension.

William thought that crying was unmanly, and when his brother, with whom he had had a close and loving relationship, died, William shed no tears. A few weeks after the funeral, however, he developed a sudden allergy which caused his eyes to water and his nasal passages to become inflamed.

It is not unusual for people who refuse to mourn to develop severe colds after a loved one has died. The colds may persist for a long time or until the individual has unconsciously satisfied a mourning period.

Serious emotional problems may also occur when no mourning takes place. Lack of mourning is an attempt to deny the death of a loved one, but this is neither realistic nor possible. Not mourning means that you are trying to maintain a relationship with a dead person. This will prevent you from having meaningful relationships with the living. Chronic depression often results from such an attempted denial of reality. You have an unresolved grief which prevents you from normal life attitudes.

If you do not mourn, you are inviting trouble. You are refusing the opportunity to ventilate your grief in an acceptable way. You are making yourself a victim of your fear of death.

On the other hand, too prolonged a period of mourning

can also leave you with psychosomatic illnesses. Concentrating all of your feelings and affections on the dead leaves you indifferent to the natural needs and claims of the living.

In the proper use of mourning, which may last as long as two years, you go through a period of concentrating your thoughts on the dead, resolving your grief, and emerging from it to resume relationships with others who need your concern and love.

If you can learn to cope emotionally and psychologically with the deaths of others, you can learn to accept the premise of your own death with dignified calmness.

How to Overcome the Fear of Your Own Death

The fear of death is really the fear of living, and you may be afraid to die because you realize that you have not yet really lived. Death is not frightening when you have lived your life to its fullest and lived each day intensely. The person who is dissatisfied and disappointed in life fears death, while the person who loves life and has had a positive contribution to make to it does not fear death.

Fear of death is fear of the unknown. But how many unknown situations have you faced and conquered in your lifetime? Fear of death is fear of darkness, but how many dark rooms have you entered in your lifetime?

Death is the other end of birth. It is part of life. When you have learned to be happy in your life, you will lose your fear of death.

XIII
A Psychosomatic Survival Kit

Say "Yes" to Life By Saying "No" to Unnecessary Illnesses

Any illness is destructive in terms of time, income, and happiness. Naturally, some illnesses and some accidents are unavoidable, but there are literally thousands of others which should never happen. The average person has many such illnesses and accidents in his lifetime. In this book we have talked about the ways in which people tend to respond to stress and to certain common life situations.

Illnesses keep you from getting the most out of life. In a sense, you are turning your back on life when you let psychosomatic illnesses take over.

In Chapter 1 we talked about the causes of psychosomatic illnesses and how emotional conflicts are expressed in physical language. Psychosomatic illnesses are caused by unhappiness, guilt, loneliness, stress, frustration, tension, and boredom. In many cases, it is not just one emotional conflict which is causing the problem, but a combination of conflicts. Usually, the psychosomatic illness is an unconscious response to those conflicts. No one deliberately decides that he is going to get sick, but he unconsciously uses sickness either as a way out of his trouble or as a way in which to avoid facing what appears to be an insolvable problem or unbearable burden.

In many cases, people unconsciously choose the physical discomfort and inconvenience of illness rather than try to resolve their particular emotional problems.

This was the case with Mrs. S., who had suffered from severe gastrointestinal trouble for over five years. She had been to a number of doctors, and on several occasions had been hospitalized for extensive tests. In addition, she had tried various patent medicines and folklore remedies, all without success. Finally it was suggested that she get psychiatric counseling before submitting to an exploratory operation.

When Mrs. S. came for consultation, she was thin and emaciated looking. She was not able to eat and she suffered from vomiting and diarrhea.

In a very real sense, she was starving herself to death, yet she insisted that she really wanted to be able to eat. Since all tests had indicated that nothing was organically wrong with Mrs. S., the real cause of her inability to keep food down had to be psychosomatic. Mrs. S. said that she had no particular problems. She had a good family relationship, lived in comfortable surroundings, and had no financial problems. Within her recent memory there had been no traumatic incidents or unusually unpleasant episodes. Neither could she recall anything specific to associate with the beginning of her stomach trouble.

It was only during psychoanalysis that the real cause of Mrs. S.'s gastrointestinal ailment was discovered. It was gradually brought out that she suffered from strong guilt feelings. These feelings were connected with an automobile accident in which Mrs. S. had been the driver. Her passenger, a friend and classmate, was killed in the accident. Mrs. S. admitted that no one blamed her for the accident, for it was not her fault, but she nevertheless felt responsible. "Had I been a more experienced driver," she explained, "I might have been able to avoid the crash."

The puzzling thing was that the accident in question had happened more than fifteen years ago, and her psychosomatic illness had not started until five years ago. She was asked to think back very carefully and try to recall just what had preceded the onset of her illness. It was obvious that she had unconsciously repressed the memory of whatever had triggered her illness.

Finally, Mrs. S. remembered that on the day preceding her first severe attack of gastrointestinal pain, she had read a very graphic description in the local paper of an accident similar to the one in which she had been involved and which had occurred in the same geographical area. Again, there was a death as a result of the accident. Thinking back, Mrs. S. remembered how upset she had become at the time she read the newspaper story.

"It all came back to me," she said. "I suddenly realized that if Audrey had not been killed in the accident, she might be a happily married woman as I am. I also thought about the fact that she might have been a mother just as I am. I felt guilty all over again, almost as if I had no right to my own happiness because I had been the cause of taking away her life. But I remember reminding myself that it was past. I burned the newspaper in the trash can, and when my husband came home from work and asked about the paper, I said we hadn't gotten any that night. I just put it out of my mind!"

Of course, the real trouble was that she hadn't put it "out" of her mind; she had simply pushed it to the back of her mind. The details of the accident which she had had and the later accident she read about were consciously forgotten, but the guilt that had been reawakened kept coming to the surface. No medicine and no surgery would ever cure Mrs. S. of her illness, since she was reacting emotionally to her guilt through her gastrointestinal system.

With treatment, Mrs. S. was able to look more closely at that accident and her part in it and accept it as a tragic but not crippling incident in her life. When she was able to do that, her gastrointestinal illness was gradually cured.

Finding the cause of your psychosomatic illness may not be very easy, and in some cases, like that of Mrs. S., professional help is needed. However, in the majority of cases, honest self-analysis will bring out the hidden cause of your psychosomatic illness. It is foolish to suffer, to deny yourself the best of life because of a psychosomatic illness.

Good Health Through Self-Analysis

In each of the preceding chapters we have attempted to point out the best means of dealing with specific psychosomatic disorders. Those are valid suggestions, but you must keep in mind that personal factors behind such symptoms differ within a narrow range from person to person. With self-analysis techniques, you can apply the best means to treat your particular psychosomatic disorder.

We must also emphasize that the first step in treating

your health problem is to be sure that any persistent symptom is completely checked out by a physician and the fact established that the symptom has no organic basis. Self-analysis is not intended to be a substitute for adequate medical care.

Assuming that you have established the precise nature of your disorder and confirmed that it is not organically based, you are ready to proceed with your self-analysis program.

Self-analysis is not mysterious or difficult. It is a form of therapy which you can use to help yourself to better health. It does require some of your time and all of your honesty. In self-analysis, you are going to be talking to yourself and you are going to be listening to yourself. There is little room for holding anything back, and no need for it. If you are not able to be honest, you are hurting yourself and prolonging your illness.

Self-analysis requires that you get to know yourself. It is a program of self-confrontation. Sometimes that act of confrontation can be very painful. In your self-analysis, you have to take into account your past, your hopes for the future, and the present. You have to be willing to see what the three components of your mind are saying and what part they play in your illness. Those components are the ego, the id, and the superego. The ego is your conscious mind and your immediate contact with reality. Your instinctual drives and desires come from your id, while your moral standards are from the superego. As we have seen in many of the case histories, when the superego's sense of guilt is too strong, self-punishing illness and accidents occur.

To start your self-analysis, you need to have a quiet place and some time to yourself. Don't be tense! Some people prefer to talk aloud to themselves, but others are too self-conscious doing this or find it inconvenient, and so they write their self-analysis. Select the method that is best for you. You may want to vary the method, using written self-analysis at times and talking at other times. I have been asked, "Why talk aloud? Isn't it good enough just to think

things through?" The purpose of talking aloud is to keep
your attention focused on your analysis. It is very easy for
the mind to waver in its attention unless definite effort is
made. Talking aloud will keep you alert, and it has the added advantage of making it more difficult for you to evade
the truth.

In carrying out your self-analysis, you should remind
yourself of your purpose, which is to discover the cause of
your psychosomatic disorder and then to help you decide
what steps you should take to make the changes necessary
to restore yourself to good health.

A Ten-Point Program for Self-Analysis

To help you in your personal self-analysis program,
here is a suggested ten-point program to follow. You may
wish to make modifications to suit your personal needs. This
program may be used for either oral or written self-analysis.
It is simply a list of vital questions that you must answer
honestly:

1. What is my health complaint?
   By this we mean that you should be specific
   about what you consider to be the cause of
   your ill health. Explain it to yourself just as
   you have to your family doctor. If you say
   that you are tired, be sure that you also consider the fact that what you may really mean
   is that you are tired because you suffer from
   sleeplessness or severe headaches. Pinpoint
   your complaint.

2. How long have I had this illness or symptom?
   Again, it is important to be very accurate
   about the length of time, since you are going
   to be looking for the specific cause.

3. When did this illness or symptom first mani-
   fest itself?

This may require some mental digging on
your part. Don't be upset if you can't immediately recall just exactly when you first felt ill.
It is not unusual for people to block out the
memory of the exact time they first began to
experience a psychosomatic illness. This unwillingness to remember is associated with its
cause.

4. What event is associated with the beginnings
of my psychosomatic disorder?
This is where the real self-analysis detective
work starts! The event is frequently a repressed memory which you will have to bring
out of your unconscious. It may be something
unpleasant or an embarrassing episode that
you are trying to forget. It may be a wrong
decision or some wrong act that your mind
has tried to ignore but can't.

5. Is there a pattern of events or behavior associated with my bouts of illness?
You may find that you are unconsciously repeating some action which makes you feel
guilty, tense, or anxious, and that this pro-
vokes your attacks of illness.

6. Is my psychosomatic disorder connected in
any way to my relationships with another person or other people?
This requires that you take an honest look at
your various interpersonal relationships. In
one case, a young wife who had psychosomatic headaches discovered that the real
cause was her dislike of her brother-in-law,
whose attitude she found overbearing and
rude. To keep peace in the family, she had
tried to ignore his unpleasant traits. Many al-

lergies are a direct result of an abrasive personal relationship.

7. What is the level of my self-esteem?
   We have already talked about the importance of having sufficient self-esteem. If you feel worthless, that will be reflected in your health. If you find that your self-esteem is low, the next step is to discover why it is low. Low self-esteem is an indication that you don't like yourself very well. At this point, you might take a look at your self-image. There is a connection between self-image and illness. Your body reflects your mental picture of yourself. Then you have to ask yourself why you have low self-esteem.

8. What gains am I getting from my illness?
   Now we are getting down to the real "nitty-gritty"! You are consciously or unconsciously receiving some kind of gain from your illness. By "gain" we mean any result which is responsible for your motivation in becoming ill or having an accident. A gain may be the fulfillment of your need for punishment. It may be an evasion of responsibility, since the illness or accident makes it impossible for you to carry out expected activities. The gain may be an increase in attention from others—mothering and acts and expressions of sympathy. Your psychosomatic illness or accident may be an overt expression of repressed hostility or tension. The relief of those feelings is a gain for you in that sense, though not a desirable one.
      It is very difficult to look into our true motivations with respect to psychosomatic disorders. It isn't pleasant to be ill at home with an upset stomach, and to have to admit that

you have made yourself miserable just because
you didn't want to attend a meeting or a social event.

9. What changes do I need to make in my life?
Once you have discovered the true cause or
causes of your psychosomatic disorder, you
will have to decide what changes should be
made. You will also have to make a priority
list for those changes.

10. How can I implement those needed changes?
Once you have listed your necessary changes
and decided in what order they should be
made, you will have to look for ways in
which to implement them. If you discover the
cause of your psychosomatic illness and decide what you should change in your life so
that you can eliminate this cause, and then
you fail to do it, you are only compounding
your original trouble.

If you have discovered that you became
violently ill after eating some meals and that
the cause was green peppers, the logical decision would be to change your diet and not eat
green peppers. You would be very foolish if,
knowing the cause, you still continue to eat
green peppers when you could substitute another food item. That is a simple example, but
the principle is the same whether the cause is
green peppers, your feelings of inadequacy,
your dislike of your mother-in-law, or anger.
Knowing what is wrong and how to handle it
is of no consequence unless you take some
form of action to overcome it.

And Finally . . .

This book was written so that you could have better
health and a more enjoyable life. Today's world imposes

many stresses, but man's response to stress through body reactions is not new. Today, however, there are probably more reasons for psychosomatic reactions than ever before. That is why it is important for you to know yourself and to know your own motivations. Face your problems, face your emotions, and learn to control situations. Don't use illness as a defense or a refuge. Despite certain literary conventions, illness does not make you more interesting. So why deliberately choose a personality which is deficient?

Self-analysis is not only a therapy to help you overcome your psychosomatic illness, it is also an excellent form of preventive therapy. If you suspect that you are on the brink of having an illness that is psychosomatic, use the technique of self-analysis to prevent that illness. If people were as interested in talking themselves out of poor health as they are willing to talk themselves into it, the incidence of sickness and accidents would be considerably less than it is.

Your health is your responsibility. If events and other people make you sick, it is because you let this happen. You have the key to your good health. Use it. Break the habit of using psychosomatic illness as your primary response to life situations.

INDEX

Accidents, psychosomatic basis of, 164–76

Acne, and masturbation guilt, 122–23

Adolescence
attitudes toward death and, 185
sex guilt and, 122–23

Aging, fear of, 178, 180–84

Allergies
as psychosomatic symptoms, 6, 121
sexual fears and, 141
of skin, 125

Anal character
development of, 48, 58
immaturity of, 143

Analyst, function of, 5

Anger
bowel dysfunction and, 59
skin conditions and, 124

Anorexia nervosa, psychosomatic illness of, 48, 53–55

Anxiety
bowel dysfunction and, 59
cardiac neurosis and, 86–89
definition of, 4
heart conditions and, 83–86
penis envy and, 152
as psychosomatic danger signal, 12–13
restlessness and, 109–11
See also Separation anxiety

Appetite loss, as psychosomatic danger signal, 12–13

Asthma, as psychosomatic symptom, 78–79

Attention, need for
accidents and, 173–75
coughing and, 72–74
obesity and, 50
scratching and, 121

Auditory symptoms, headaches and, 44

Bible, the, attitude toward menstruation in, 146–47

Blood pressure, 6
as psychosomatic illness, 82, 89–91

Body-chatter
colds and, 20
decoding of, 6
definition of, 5
as primary gain, 61

Bowel dysfunction
anxiety and, 59–61
as psychosomatic illness, 48

Breathing problem, 6
as psychosomatic illness, 74–80

Broken heart, as psychosomatic cause, 93–95

Bronchitis, as psychosomatic symptom, 78

Calendars (time), and colds, 25

Calvinist work doctrine, 100–1

Cardiac neurosis (cardiophobia), anxiety and, 86–89

Castration anxiety (castration complex), formation of, 138–40

Cervantes, Miguel de, 37, 98

Change factor, and colds, 26

Chest pains, as psychosomatic symptom, 6

Childhood
attitudes toward death and, 185
separation anxiety during, 22

Children
emotional outlets available to, 5
headaches among, 40–42

Climacteric, 160–61

Colds, 16–29
body-chatter and, 20
change factor and, 26–27
contagious nature of, 27
depression and, 24
prevention of, 27–29
separation anxiety and, 20–23
susceptibility to, 16–20

Unconscious
accidents, 167, 170, 175
definition of, 3
id and superego relation to, 35
repression and, 23
Urination, as psychosomatic symptom, 6
Urticaria, *see* Hives

Vaginal itching, and sex guilt,
120–21
Vitamin C, colds and, 18
Vomiting, children's anxiety and, 5

Watts, Isaac, 102
Weight problems, as psychosomatic
symptom, 52
Wetting, children's anxiety and,
5
Witch doctors, psychosomatic illness
and, 8–9
Women
menopause among, 154–60
menstrual period of, 26, 146–
56
as secondary citizens, 150–53
sex role and, 140–42